Finding Out About Textiles

Gillian Jones

Head of Textiles, Newcastle-under-Lyme School

Series editor: Valda Reynolds

Stanley Thornes (Publishers) Ltd

First published in 1990 by
Stanley Thornes (Publishers) Ltd
Old Station Drive
Leckhampton
CHELTENHAM GL53 0DN
England

Reprinted 1993

British Library Cataloguing in Publication Data

Jones, Gillian
    Finding out about textiles
    1. Textiles
    I. Title
    677

    ISBN 0-7487-0179-6

Typeset by Tech-Set, Gateshead, Tyne & Wear
Printed and bound in Great Britain at The Bath Press, Avon

Acknowledgements

The author and publishers would like to thank the following for their help in the production of this book: Graham Jones for proof reading and photographs; pupils of Newcastle-under-Lyme school for photographs on pages 16, 19, 139, 141, 142, 148; Janet Singleton for her help with computing; Mrs M Knox of Courtaulds Jersey, Leek, Staffs for photographs on pages 79, 91, 94.

We would like to thank the following for permission to reproduce previously published material and photographs: The Advertising Standards Authority (p. 121); Albright and Wilson Ltd (p. 95); Bernina (p. 43, top left); The Advisory Unit for Microtechnology in Education; Wm. Briggs and Co (p. 153); British Wool Marketing Board (p. 57, top left); Brother (p. 79); BTTG (p. 58, 59, 60, 61, 64, 75, 78); Dylon International Ltd (p. 24, 27, 28, 29, 37); The Harris Tweed Association Ltd (p. 57); Husqvarna-Viking Ltd (p. 43, top right); International Wool Secretariat (p. 13, 14, 40, 56); The Office of Fair Trading, Crown Copyright (p. 130); Manchester Art Galleries (p. 23); Marks and Spencer plc (p. 65, right, p. 81); New Home (p. 42, 46); The Photo Co-op (p. 16, top); Popperphoto (p. 15, bottom); Prima (p. 89); Shetland Knitwear Trades Association (p. 57, bottom left); Simplicity and Style patterns (p. 48, 49); Sire Records Company (p. 15, top); Claire Starkey (p. 112); Peter Storm (p. 99); Which magazine, July 1987 (p. 131); Wyvern Yarns (p. 22).

Every effort has been made to trace copyright holders and we apologise if any have been overlooked.

Contents

How to use this book

Finding Out About Textiles has been designed to have an emphasis on active learning with a high degree of pupil involvement. The **Guidance** chapter at the beginning of the book explains the **skills** required for studying Textile courses; analysing, researching, designing, investigating and recording information, making decisions, planning and evaluating work.

The rest of the book is divided into three **study areas** each of which is subdivided into three **units**.

Each unit provides:

● a **core information** section

● a **pupil participation** section in the form of **working briefs** and **written work**.

You will be able to add to the core information with research of your own to complete the work in this section. The work includes: discussions, surveys, investigations, fact-finding exercises, data response and free response questions.

As you complete each unit you should fill in a **self-assessment chart** and **self-marking plan** for that unit, so that you can assess your own progress. Copymasters of these forms are provided on pages 161 and 162 for you to photocopy.

Appendices appear at the end of each study area. These give examples of methods of recording and presenting results. A **resource guide** accompanies each study area and includes useful addresses, reference books, teaching aids available, videos and computer software.

The **link-up charts** on pages 163–8 show how the subjects covered in this book are linked to the other common elements of GCSE Home Economics: Home, Food and Child Development. The charts also show at a glance which common themes and skills required for GCSE are provided in each study area.

Guidance

Common elements and common themes

Textiles is one of the **four main aspects** of Home Economics. The others are **Home, Food** and **Child Development**.
When Textiles is the main study the other three are known as the **common elements**.

All these aspects are interrelated and it is necessary to include all of them when studying Textiles and to include information from all the common elements in coursework and theory work.
All four main aspects are brought together by **seven common themes**. These are: 1. Human Development   2. Health   3. Safety and Protection
4. Efficiency   5. Values   6. Aesthetics   7. Interaction with the Environment.

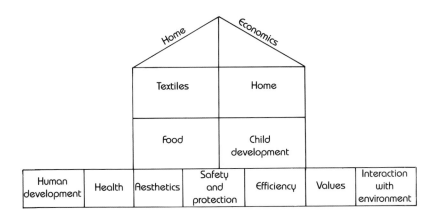

These seven themes form the essential study bases for all four aspects of Home Economics. The link-up charts at the end of the book show clearly these interrelationships.

The subject of Textiles is both practical and theoretical and the two aspects are linked through skills which are associated with the management and organisation of resources.

The skills will be helpful to you throughout your life both as an individual and as a member of a family or a community.

Skills

The **skills** which are needed when studying Textiles are:
- investigation   • measurement   • communication   • management
- psycho-motor   • technological   • interpersonal.

You will need to:
analyse ⟶ research ⟶ record ⟶ investigate ⟶ decide ⟶
plan ⟶ execute ⟶ evaluate.

By following this process you will be using and developing important skills.

Analysis

This is an important skill and practice will help you to understand what is needed. When presented with an assignment or brief, you must:

- Read the wording carefully in order to think about the underlying factors that will have to be thought about in planning.
- Write down what the assignment is actually asking you to do.
- Consider the seven common themes in relation to the brief.
- Keep in mind any constraints or restrictions that you may have.

Brief analysis

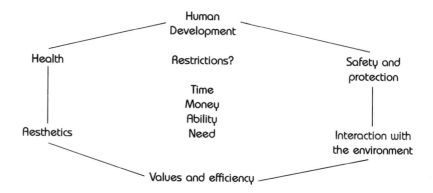

Research

Finding out about new facts or increasing your knowledge of known facts will involve collecting together information from many different sources such as leaflets, booklets, magazines, books, worksheets, information sheets, audio and video tapes, catalogues, pictures, photographs, visits to museums, art galleries, mills, factories, inviting people to speak, watching TV programmes, using computer software, visiting shops, stores and supermarkets, using libraries and reference material.

Remember to:

- Write polite letters when requesting information and include a stamped addressed envelope for a reply.
- Ask politely for assistance in libraries, book shops, museums etc.
- Request permission to visit factories, study centres, stores etc.
- Use your time sensibly when on a visit and make a note of important points.
- Say thank you for any help which is given to you.

Designing

Your research may require you to design an article or garment or work a decorative motif as a design.

If you enjoy designing this will be easy for you to do, but you may need to consider the different types of design that are possible:

Natural

Designs can be taken straight from nature:

- Collect items such as shells, bark, driftwood, feathers, stones, seeds, leaves etc.
- Draw plants, trees, flowers, animals, birds and insects.
- Sketch scenery, landscapes and seascapes.
- Refer to biology books for sketches of cells.

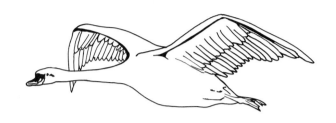

Geometrical

Designs can be created from geometrical shapes:

- triangles   ● diamonds   ● squares   ● rectangles   ● circles
- segments etc.

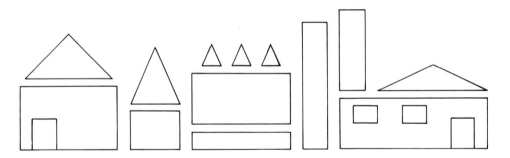

Abstract

Designs which do not represent any recognisable form or shape are described as abstract. They can be achieved by:

- doodles   ● scribbles   ● splatter effects   ● blobs   ● torn shapes.

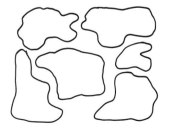

3

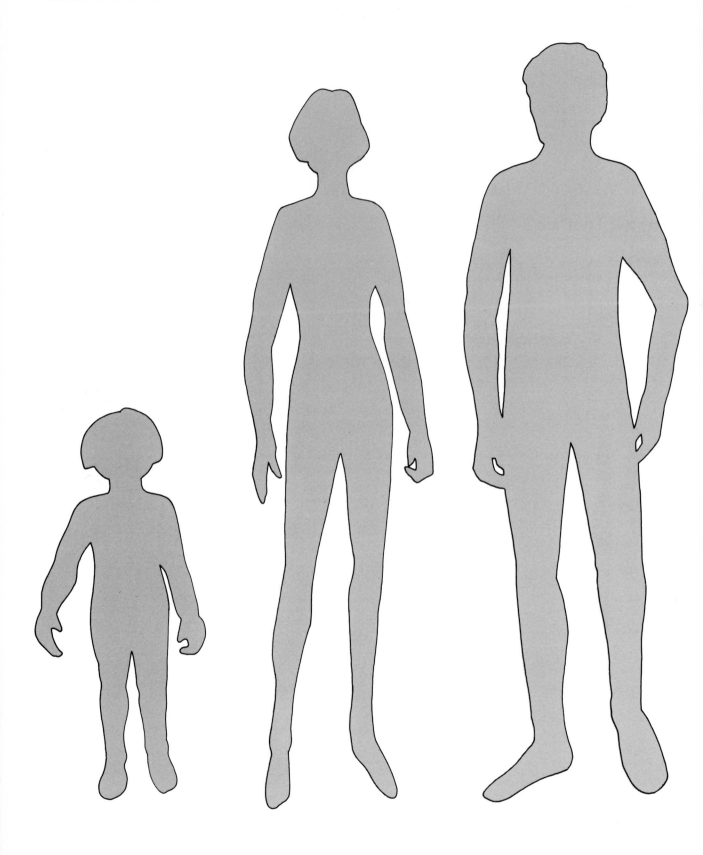

You may need to draw figure shapes when illustrating garments. Practice will improve your sketches but if you cannot draw well then use a template shape such as those illustrated and use them to give you the outline on which to put clothes.

As designing may come into many of your assignments it is helpful to:
● Collect ideas for designs from magazines, books, nature, etc.
● Keep a sketch pad with drawings and doodles in it.
● Practise figure drawing.
● Study how clothes hang, how pleats, gathers and flares alter hemlines.
● Collect pictures of up-to-date fashions.

Investigation

Textiles can be investigated scientifically or creatively. The two different approaches are equally important and require skill. The scientific approach will require you to carry out experiments with fibres, yarns and fabrics.

The design approach will require you to experiment with different techniques or methods of construction.

Whichever approach you use you will have to:
● Organise your experiments.
● Observe the results.
● Draw conclusions.

Record what you see soon afterwards or you may forget the details. Work accurately, concentrate on what you are doing and be interested in your work.

Recording information

Research and investigation will require you to record information and there are many ways of doing this:
● Provide a written account in your own words.
● Use sketches, drawings, diagrams, graphs, charts, pie charts and flow charts.

Make your work interesting by using a variety of methods but ensure that it is:
● clear ● neat ● concise ● well written or typed ● audible on tape ● on suitable paper ● well presented ● interesting to read ● well illustrated ● relevant ● original.

Surveys and market research are useful ways of collecting information. For example, you could do a survey of pupils in your school.

Query – Do you prefer man-made fabrics to natural fabrics?

Result:

	No			*Yes*			*Sometimes*	
ЖНТ	ЖНТ	ЖНТ	ЖНТ	ЖНТ	ЖНТ		ЖНТ	ЖНТ
	20			10			10	

The results can be shown in different ways:

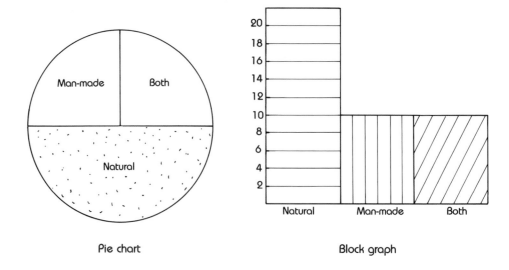

Pie chart   Block graph

The results of an experiment to show the thermal conductivity of different fibres could be shown as a line graph:

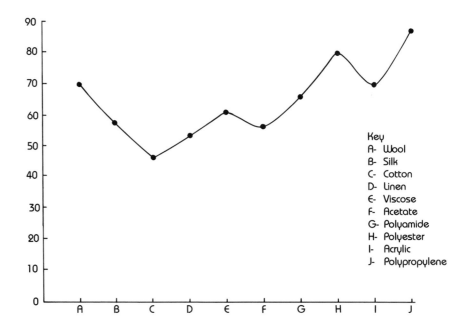

Key
A- Wool
B- Silk
C- Cotton
D- Linen
E- Viscose
F- Acetate
G- Polyamide
H- Polyester
I- Acrylic
J- Polypropylene

Decisions

Having researched and investigated you will be expected to make several decisions based on your information and the results of your experiments. Several possible alternatives may be available but you must consider which is the most suitable fabric, method, design, thread, colour etc. Do not forget to give reasons for your choice.

Planning an order of work

You may have to work out a step-by-step procedure for completing an assignment. Work it out in rough first, putting the processes in a numbered order and altering it until you are satisfied that you have the best way of doing it.

The presentation of your order of work could be done in different ways:

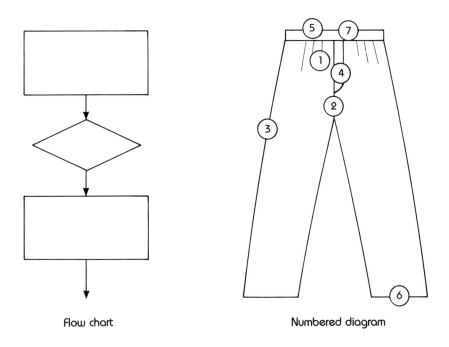

Flow chart   Numbered diagram

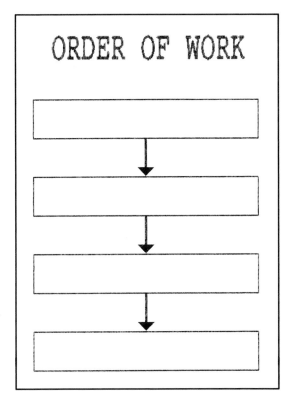

Computer print-out

Evaluation

In order to evaluate your work you must be honest with yourself and criticise your work. No work is perfect and most things can be improved in one way or another. Ask yourself some questions and give reasons for your replies:

- Was your planning good enough?
- Could things have worked out better if they had been done another way?
- What do you honestly think of the result?
- What would you change if you did it again?
- What did you find difficult to do?
- Were your decisions correct or did you make the wrong choices?
- Could you still improve the result at this stage?
- Could the assignment be developed further?
- How could you use the knowledge that you have gained?
- Was the assignment a successful one?

During your course you will be required to use and develop skills in all these different areas and these will be tested in your coursework and theory paper.

Methodology

In this book a variety of different ways of tackling your work are suggested. Each working brief is clearly marked with the methodology to be used. They include:

- brain storming   • class and discussion groups   • role play   • triggers
- guest speakers   • visits   • questionnaires   • surveys
- investigations   • experiments   • community work   • problem solving assignments   • posters and display work   • debates   • market research   • varied group work.

Symbols appear in the pupil participation sections to indicate that the task should be done with the aid of a video [◎▯] or a computer [▯] .

Fashion and clothing

UNIT ONE

Fashion

Study
Area 1

Core information

Reasons for wearing clothes

Clothing is worn to:

- protect the body
- cover the body for modesty
- decorate the body for attraction
- identify occupations
- show status in society
- identify groups in society.

Arabian *kibr*

Sealskin parkas

Protection

- Our bodies need protection from extremes of temperature. In colder countries people wear furs and skins for warmth. Hot climates demand a different type of garment which is long and loose to allow air to circulate. Traditional saris, sarongs and kimonos are examples of these.
- We need to protect our bodies from injury and clothing can protect us from accidents that could seriously damage our bodies. Motor cycle leathers, skate-boarding padded garments and flame-proof motor racing overalls all serve this purpose.
- Industrial workers need protection from machinery, sparks and chemicals. Construction workers wear helmets and steel toe-caps on their boots for protection.
- Workers in food industries are required to wear protective clothing such as aprons, overalls, head coverings and gloves for reasons of hygiene.

Modesty

- Ideas of modesty vary according to culture. In the Middle East women have to appear modest in public, especially in the presence of men. Garments which hide the body shape are worn, for example, the Moslem *burka*, the Algerian *haik* and the *yashmak*. Tourists are often asked to cover themselves when going into towns and especially into religious buildings as a mark of respect.
- In Britain earlier this century, modesty vests were worn to conceal the chest in low necklines and long skirts hid female legs.

Burka

Attraction

- In nature the male of the species is often more attractive, for example, the lion with its mane and the peacock with its tail.
- In the seventeenth and eighteenth centuries men wore silks and velvets trimmed with lace and frills. The doublet and hose illustrated shows a different male image than is seen today.
- Women have taken over this attraction role and are generally more decorative than men.

Doublet and hose

Duke of Burgundy 1695

Occupation

- Work demands practical and comfortable clothes and certain occupations have an easily identifiable uniform, for example, people working for the Police, the Fire Service and the Post Office.
- A policeman or woman's uniform shows their authority as well as their occupation.
- A nurse's uniform serves two purposes, cleanliness and role recognition.

- Judges and barristers wear wigs and gowns in court to denote their profession and role and mayors wear chains of office and ceremonial dress on special occasions.

Judge's wig

Status

- In our society possessions show social status, as do well cut designer label clothes made from quality fabrics.

Groups in Society

- Different nationalities and cultures may be identified by their traditional garments.
- Uniforms can also identify groups such as Guides, Scouts and the Armed Services.
- Group dressing can be seen in teenagers, for example, punks, hippies and fan club members.
- In school uniforms it can foster a group feeling and overcome social differences.

Clothing is also influenced by:

- lifestyle ● economic factors ● age ● sex ● physical build.

Fashion

Fashion is a change of taste and style. Each period in history has a definite style which can be seen in:

- architecture ● art ● clothes ● decoration ● domestic articles
- furniture.

Look at the items illustrated from 1860 and find a similar shape in them all.

Fashion changes rapidly and when a fashion has been accepted by all, it will be replaced by a new style which is then 'fashionable'. We follow fashion because:

● we like change   ● we tire of styles   ● we are anxious to keep ahead of our friends   ● we do not want to appear 'old fashioned'.

Who decides what will be fashionable?

● Fashion designers suggest what we should wear.
● Manufacturers decide which styles to make.
● Magazines and newspapers report fashion trends.
● The public decides which styles to wear.

Fashion has always had its leaders and royalty led fashion for many years until it became more accessible to everyone.

Haute couture

● The term 'haute couture' means exclusive fashion by top designers.
● A couturier is a male fashion designer and a couturière is a female designer.
● The place where they work is called a fashion house, for example, House of Dior
● Designers make two collections or ranges of garments each year.
● The collections are modelled to the press and public.
● There are four main centres of fashion – Paris, London, New York and Milan.

Designers of Haute Couture

American Calvin Klein, Ralph Lauren, Anne Klein, Bill Blass, Roy Halston.
Italian Gianni Versace, Georgio Armani, Valentino Garavani, Tai Missoni.
British Katharine Hamnett, Jasper Conran, John Galliano, Bruce Oldfield.
French Yves St. Laurent, Jean Paul Gaultier, Karl Lagerfeld.
Japanese Issey Miyake, Johji Yamamoto, Kenzo Takada, Rei Kawakubo.

Many designers have 'diffusion' ranges or cheaper garments for:

● people who cannot afford expensive prices, for example, Emporio Armani
● young people who want designer clothes, for example, Junior Gaultier.

Haute Couture is:

● very expensive   ● very exclusive   ● copied for everyday fashion.

Designer outfits

The fashion business

Fashion is big business. It is Britain's third most important manufacturing industry and a lot of money is invested in it. It employs 9% of Britain's work-force and is very important for the export trade.

The flow chart shows the chain of trade in the textile industry from fibre molecule to consumer.

The fashion business becomes part of the chain when the fabric is used for a new design.

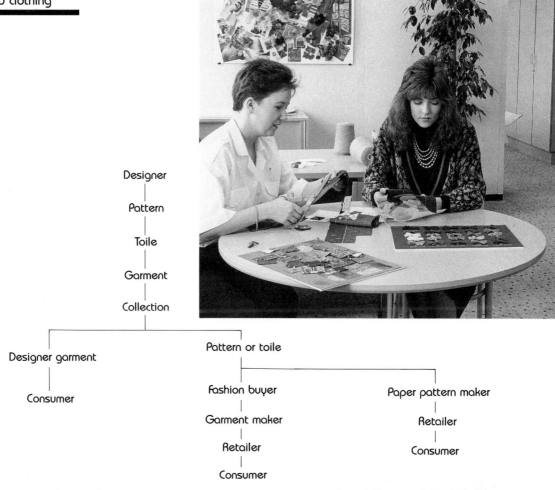

```
                    Designer
                       |
                    Pattern
                       |
                     Toile
                       |
                    Garment
                       |
                   Collection
        _____|_____
       |                                           |
Designer garment                           Pattern or toile
       |                          _____|_____
   Consumer                      |                                   |
                            Fashion buyer                   Paper pattern maker
                                 |                                   |
                            Garment maker                        Retailer
                                 |                                   |
                              Retailer                           Consumer
                                 |
                              Consumer
```

14

Designer   The person who sketches the original garment.
Pattern   The design translated into paper pieces.
Toile   A calico model of the design.
Designer garment   The original garment made by the designer.
Fashion buyer   An employee of a fashion manufacturer who buys designs from the designers with a view to making the designs up for sale to the public.
Manufacturer   A firm who mass produces a ready-to-wear version.
Wholesaler   A firm who acts as middle-man between the manufacturer and the retailer.
Retailer   The seller of the garment to the consumer.
Consumer   The buyer of the garment.

Not all fashions come from famous designers. Designers working for manufacturers get their inspiration from many sources:

- Designers: Georgio Armani, Yves St. Laurent etc.
- Street fashion: Jeans, ethnic styles
- Music business: Bros, Madonna
- Films: Out of Africa
- Sport: cycle shorts
- New technology: ice-wash denim
- Politics and economy: lifestyle
- Personalities: royalty.

Street fashion

Finding out about the history of fashion

Anyone for tennis?

The photographs on the left show two completely different styles of teenage dress. Can you suggest a date for the bottom photograph? Old photographs can be a useful source of information when studying fashion. The history of fashion can be studied by looking at:

● photographs ● paintings ● fashion plates ● cartoons ● films and TV productions.

Books and magazines are a useful resource:

● Novels – Jane Austen, Charles Dickens, W.M. Thackeray
● Fashion reference books (refer to the Resources guide on page 53)
● Textile Society magazines
● Old magazines – *Woman's Own, Vogue, Woman's Weekly.*

Visit places where actual costume can be seen:

● museums and art galleries ● antique's fairs ● exhibitions and collections.

Pupil participation ─────────────

Working briefs

1. Clothing   Group work (Display)

Take part in a discussion of why people wear clothes and then find pictures of clothing which come under any of the following headings:

● Warmth
● Protection
● Workwear
● Sportswear
● Fashion.

Make a display with the pictures using the five headings.

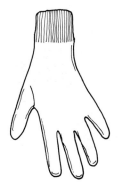   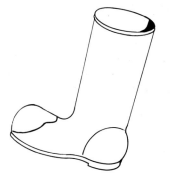

2. Clothing styles
Group work (Discussion)

Discuss in small groups the meaning of the following types of clothing styles and suggest examples of each type:

● Traditional
● Casual
● Functional
● Fashionable.

Appoint a spokesperson for each group to report back to the class.

Summarise the characteristics of each style of clothing with a final class discussion.

3. Fashion history Individual work (Investigation and display)

Bring into school any pictures which show fashions of the past. Find out the dates of the styles shown by looking in fashion reference books (see the book list on page 53).

Discuss your pictures in a group discussion and make up a display of them in date order. Pictures could include photographs, illustrations, birthday cards, paintings, Christmas cards etc.

4. Fashion interview
Class work (Questionnaire)

Prepare a list of questions that you could ask elderly relatives or older adults about the clothes that they wore as children and teenagers. Include questions about their wedding outfits and also ask how they feel about today's fashions. (A sample questionnaire is provided in the Appendices on page 50).

Carry out the interview with several adults, recording their replies and report back to the class with your findings.

5. Uniform
Class work (Debate and design)

Uniform should be worn for school.

a) Make a list of points agreeing and disagreeing with this statement.
b) Take part in a class debate which puts forward both sides of the argument.
c) Design a school uniform for the year 2000.
   Give reasons for your choice.

6. Traditional dress   Class work (Guest speaker)

Write a letter to a person of Asian origin in your local community and ask if they would be willing to come and talk to your group about their traditional dress.

Arrange a date and time that is convenient for you both. Offer to act as a host or hostess on the day or to thank the speaker after the talk.

After the talk write an account of the clothing discussed and sketch the items and label them.

7. Choosing clothes   Individual work
(Problem solving and design)

Assignment A   Helen is going shopping for a new outfit. She is quite tall and slim with fair hair and blue eyes. Design an outfit for a party to suit her size, shape and colouring.

Assignment B   Jim is a well-built boy who likes casual clothes. Design a party outfit for him as well. He has dark hair and brown eyes and is of average height.

Both designs could be done using the computer program 'Fads' (refer to the Resources guide on page 54). Print out the two in their party wear.

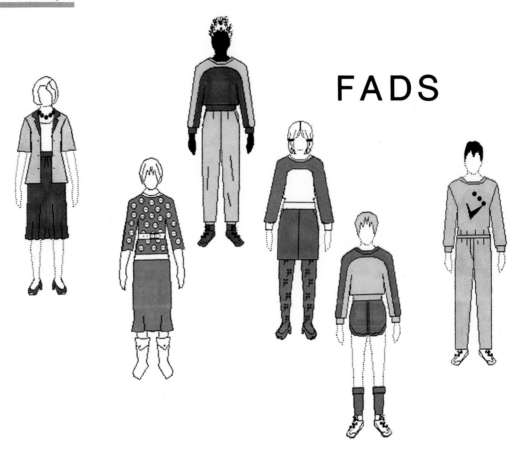

FADS

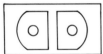

8. The fashion business   Class (Video and questionnaire)

Watch the video *Fashion Means Business* produced by the Design Council. The video shows how fashion designs are produced and sold. The business side of fashion is emphasised by following the collection of a young designer from the original design to the consumer.

Questions can be found in the Appendices on page 51 to be answered after the video has been watched.

Written work

Fact finding exercise

Here is a list of traditional garments:

● sari   ● sarong   ● kimono   ● kaftan   ● kilt   ● poncho.

Copy out and fill in the chart below for each of these garments.

Garment	Description	Country of origin	Fabric	Decoration

Application of knowledge

Study the picture of a lifeboat crew and write about:

1. The function of their clothing

2. The colour of their clothing

3. The fabric of their clothing.

Problem solving

You have been given a six metre length of fabric which you must not cut. It is a plain coloured cotton, one metre wide.

Design a fashionable garment based on a traditional style to use the piece of fabric. Sketch the garment and suggest a design that could be printed onto the fabric to add to the decoration of the garment.

Structured questions

Paris is the centre of Haute Couture.

1. What is meant by the term 'Haute Couture'?

2. Name two other centres of fashion in Europe.

3. Name four famous couturiers.

4. Explain the terms:
   a) Mass produced clothing
   b) Made-to-measure garments
   c) Off-the-peg garments.

5. Describe the chain of trade for a garment from fibre to consumer.

6. Fashion changes very rapidly. Give reasons why this happens and give examples of changing fashion in the past few years.

MORE DESIGNER SENSATIONS

More stunning designer Knit-Kits from Wyvern, in super soft yarns and great value from only £18.95

Choose from five designs, featuring the new seasons top colours in wool rich yarn with the look of Mohair. Ideal for Spring days and Summer evenings.

These specially commissioned designs use simple stitches throughout and the complete kit includes full instructions, yarn and viscose ribbon.

Each design is only available in the colourway shown and in Small, Medium and Large sizes.

With each order we will send you, completely free, our full colour catalogue of 40 further exciting Summer designs. Or you can obtain this catalogue by sending £1.50 which will be refunded with your first order.

To order simply fill in the coupon below and send with your cheque/Postal Order to

Wyvern Yarns
2 TUER WAY,
INKBERROW,
WORCS. WR7 4EQ
Regd. No: 2023578
☎ TELEPHONE ORDERS
0527 68777 (24 hour service)

DELIVERY
All orders
despatched in 7 days.
Allow 28 days
for delivery.
GUARANTEE
Full refund
if kit returned
unused within
14 days.

Please indicate quantity, size and design required in the space provided	30/32"	34/36"	38/40"
	Small	Medium	Large
525 Candy Floss			
526 Fiesta			
527 Charisma			
528 Nocturne			
529 Gypsy			
Price	£18.95	£21.45	£24.45

Please add £2.20 post and packing per kit.

NAME _____

ADDRESS _____

POST CODE _____ Catalogue at £1.50 ☐

PR2

22

This advertisement is for designer Knit-kits.

1. a) How many designs are available?
   b) How much money would you send for a medium size design 528?
   c) Describe the two possible ways of ordering a kit?
   d) What guarantee is given in the advertisment?
   e) How can you obtain a catalogue?

2. Why is wool an ideal yarn for the sweaters?

3. Sketch a care label which could be put inside the completed sweater.

4. The kits are described as 'Designer Sensations'. Explain what you understand by this description.

Free response

The illustration shows a painting called 'Along the Shore' by J.E. Southall.

Discuss the value of paintings and prints for studying costume and suggest other ways of finding out about fashion.

Self-assessment

Photocopy and complete the self-assessment chart on page 161, inserting the following list of topics under 'The work I have done includes':

1. Reasons for wearing clothes
2. Traditional styles
3. Casual and functional clothing
4. Fashion
5. Haute couture
6. The fashion business
7. The psychology of clothes
8. Finding out about fashion.

Photocopy and complete the self-marking plan on page 162 for the seven working briefs in this unit.

UNIT TWO

You and your clothes

Core information ─────────────

Colour, line, pattern and texture

In order to look our best we should:

● emphasise our good points ● disguise our bad points.

This can be done by thinking about:

● line ● colour ● pattern ● texture.

Skilful use of these four considerations can create illusions so that the eye is tricked into seeing things which are flattering to the wearer.

Colour

Colour has always been important for clothing.

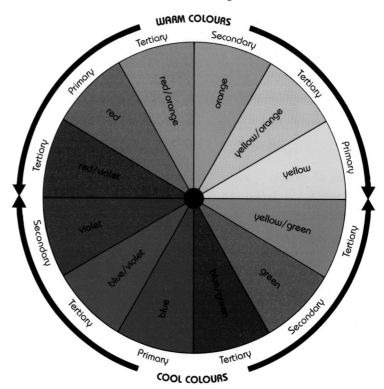

A study of the colour wheel above will reveal:

● All colours come from three **primary** colours, these are red, blue and yellow.
● Two primary colours mix together to make a **secondary** colour, for example, red + yellow = orange, red + blue = violet, blue + yellow = green.

- A primary and a secondary colour mix together to make a **tertiary** colour, for example, blue + green = turquoise.
- Opposite colours on the circle are **complementary** or **contrasting**.
- **Toning** colours are found next to each other on the circle.
- **Warm** colours contain yellow or red.
- **Cold** colours contain blue.

Knowing these facts it is possible to create harmony and illusion with colour.

- Toning colours are harmonious and pleasing to the eye.
- Discordant colours are ones which do not go well together.
- Contrasting colours complement each other.
- Strong bright colours attract attention to size and shape.
- Dark shades have a slimming effect.
- Tints have an enlarging effect.
- Black, white and grey bring out the brightness in colour.

Colour and its effect

Colour is all around us, it is important to our lives. Colour is used to:

- Signify events in life such as black for deaths and white for weddings.
- Suggest feelings such as red for danger, yellow for cowardice, green for envy and black for depression.
- Assist body healing with colour therapy; blue for the throat, green for the heart and lungs and yellow for the digestion.
- Sell goods by attracting customers towards the packaging in the supermarket by using bright colours such as red, blue and yellow.
- Protect the body when it is worn as safety wear in fluorescent armbands, coloured jackets and yellow safety helmets.
- Improve the environment when used on doors, window frames, interior decorations and furnishings.
- Stimulate the appetite when used in food presentation.
- Decorate our bodies with make-up, clothes and hair colourings.

Choosing colours

Everyone has a range of colours which suits them and these are controlled by three things:

- the tone of your skin
- the colour of your eyes
- the colour of your hair.

Choice of colour is a personal matter but guidelines can be followed so that you can make the best of yourself. These are shown in the chart below.

Skin	Eyes	Hair	Choose	Avoid
Pale Peach	Blue Green Grey	Blonde Honey Light Golden	Medium shades Warm colours	Pale shades Vivid colours
Pale Pink	Green Blue Hazel	Mousy Light brown	Light/medium shades	Harsh/drab colours
Cream Olive Rosy	Dark Brown Hazel Blue Grey	Dark brown Black	Bright/Clear colours	Yellow Muddy shades
Fair	Blue Hazel Green Grey	Red Auburn	Blues Greens Dark shades	Harsh/Bright colours Reds

When choosing colours:

- Check the colour against your skin, hair and eyes.
- If in doubt, start with a basic colour such as black, navy, beige or brown and add colour with accessories.
- Choose colours which flatter you.
- Choose colours that you feel comfortable in.
- Do not mix too many colours together.

Colour consultancies have been set up to advise people about which colours to wear. The ranges that they suggest are often linked to a season of the year, spring, summer, autumn or winter colours. Remember that colour is part of the fashion scene and following colour fashion can be as expensive as being a slave to fashion styles.

Adding colour to your clothing

Colour can be added to your clothes to make them individual by:

- dyeing with commercial dyes
- dyeing with natural dyes
- tie-dyeing
- tritik
- batik
- fabric painting
- fabric paints
- appliqué
- hand embroidery
- machine embroidery.

Commercial dyes

Dyes like the ones illustrated can be bought to use at home. There are:

- natural fabric dyes • multi-purpose dyes • cold water dyes • washing machine dyes.

Rules

- Choose a type of dye suitable for the fibre of the garment.
- Buy enough dye for the dry weight of the garment.
- Check to see if you need a fixing substance (salt or dye-fix).
- Follow the instructions on the pack.

Natural dyes

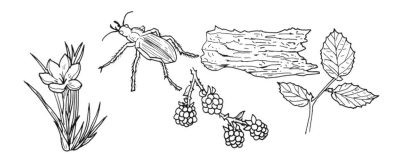

Dyes can be made from all the things illustrated and natural dyeing is an ancient craft used for colouring fabric. Anyone can make a dye from most natural substances by cutting them up and boiling them in water. The resulting liquid is the dye solution after it has been sieved.

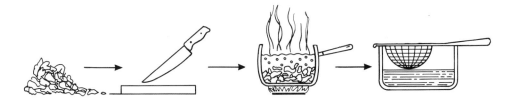

Sometimes a **mordant** is needed to make the dye hold in the fabric. Mordants are chemicals which act as fixing agents and they include:

Alum Chrome Tin Copper Iron

Take care when using these chemicals as they are poisonous. The mordant is added to the dye solution or the fibre is treated with a mordant solution before dyeing.

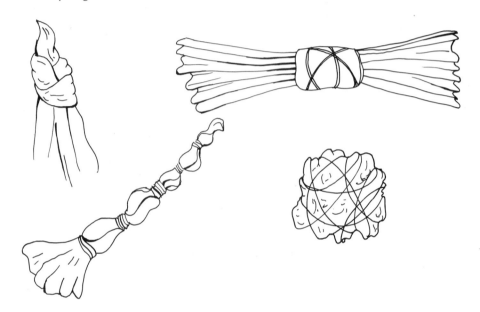

Tie-dyeing

There are different ways of tying the fabric in preparation for the dyeing such as:

● pleating or folding before tying very firmly   ● crumpling and fastening into a ball shape   ● tying the fabric tightly in knots   ● twisting the fabric and wrapping thread or elastic bands around it.

The picture shows where the dye solution has been absorbed and where the tied parts have resisted the dye to produce a design on the fabric. Tie-dyeing is a **resist** method of dyeing.

Tritik

Tritik is another method of resist dyeing. The fabric is gathered up tightly to make it resist the dye solution.

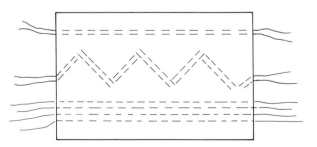

The diagram shows how the fabric is stitched with rows of thread to make the design.

- Strong thread is needed to that it can be pulled tightly.
- Single or double rows can be stitched.
- A design can be planned or it can be random.
- After stitching pull the thread and end it off or knot it.
- Dye the fabric when it is all gathered up and remove the thread when it is dry.

Batik

This is the name given to a wax resist method of colouring fabric. You will need the following equipment:

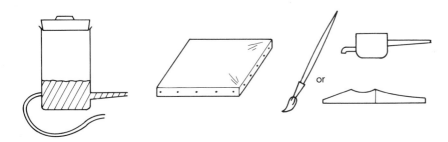

The wax is melted and put onto the parts of the fabric where colour is not wanted. It is necessary to stretch the fabric onto a frame to keep it taut and to paint the wax on with a brush or tjanting tool as illustrated. When the painting is completed the fabric is dyed and the wax resists the colour to leave white areas when it is removed.

Fabric printing

Colour can be printed onto fabric using:

- blocks made from lino, potato or wood   ● stencils of card or metal   ● spraying techniques   ● transfers linked with special inks or crayons   ● fabric paints   ● screen printing   ● fabric felt pens.

 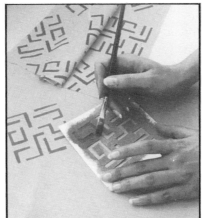 

- Each method requires different equipment.
- Check the fibre content and see if the printing material is correct for it.
- Follow the instructions for the method used.
- Check if the design has to be 'fixed' before use.

Fabric paints

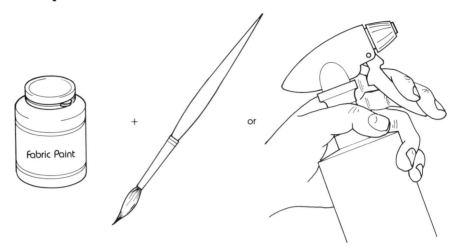

There are special fabric paints which can give different finishes such as metallic, fluorescent and opaque. They are painted directly onto the fabric and are fixed by ironing.

Appliqué

- Colour can be added to garments by appliquéd designs as in the picture.
- Appliqué is achieved by adding fabric onto a background fabric to make a motif which is held in place by hand or machine stitching.
- Fraying fabric can be backed with iron-on interfacing before cutting.

Hand embroidery

- Colour can be given to a garment by decorating it with hand embroidery stitching.
- There are many different stitches as shown in the diagrams.

- A design often consists of a combination of stitches.
- Different thicknesses of thread can be used.

Machine embroidery

Embroidery can be worked on the ordinary sewing machine using a basic straight stitch. The designs below are all line designs in straight stitching:

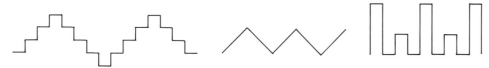

Electronically controlled machines have a variety of stitches which can be used for decoration. The zig-zag stitch is illustrated.

Programmable computerised machines or 'creative computers' can create coloured embroidery at the touch of a button. Letters, numbers, flowers, animal shapes, borders and motifs are possible. Examples are illustrated from the *Newhome®* machine.

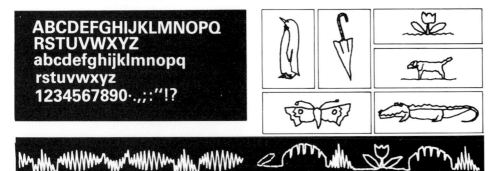

Free machine embroidery can be done on all types of machine since it needs no special stitches.

- It is worked in a hoop as the fabric needs to be drum-tight.
- The teeth of the machine are dropped or covered to prevent movement.
- The stitch length is reduced to nil.
- The design is created by the movement of the hoop under a fast-moving needle.
- Some possible effects are shown here.

Line

Styles are created from lines:

- Outside lines create the silhouette.
- Inside lines create detail, for example, seams, waistlines and darts.

Look at the lines illustrated:

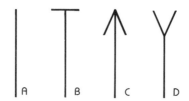

The eye tricks you into thinking that they are different lengths. These lines can be seen as detail lines on garments.

- Line A allows the eye to travel upwards without interruption; it gives an impression of height.
- Line B shortens the figure since the eye stops at the top of the line and moves sideways.
- Line C shortens it even more as the eye is drawn downwards.
- Line D gives the best illusion of height as the eye continues to travel upwards from the top of the line.

Stripes can create illusion and as a general rule:
- Vertical lines or stripes make things look taller.
- Horizontal lines or stripes make things look wider.
- Narrow stripes are more flattering.
- Wide stripes add width.

Pattern

Pattern should be used with body size in mind. Notice the use of narrow stripes on the smallest child and broader stripes on the mother. The effect of pattern size is important for a flattering appearance:
- Large designs emphasise large shapes.
- Small designs suit small figures.
- Small designs can flatter a larger figure shape.
- Large designs can dwarf a small figure.

Care should be taken with checks, plaids, large prints and stripes. Study their effect on different body sizes and look at how the design is placed on the figure.

Texture

Texture can be:
- soft • stiff • rough • smooth • hard • shiny • dull
- ribbed • nobbly • hairy.

Texture adds bulk and increases size. A bulky fabric gives an increased width to the body and textured fabrics should be used with care. The following fabrics are typical textured fabrics:
- Velour – soft • Tafetta – stiff • Hessian – rough
- Silk – smooth • Linen – hard • Satin – shiny • Denim – dull
- Corduroy – ribbed • Crêpe – nobbly • Mohair – hairy.

Shiny fabrics are not bulky but they reflect light and flatter only a good shape. They draw attention to less than perfect shapes.

Pupil participation

Working briefs

1. Colour, pattern, line, texture
Individual work (Investigation)

Make a figure comparison window as described in the Appendices on page 52. Use the windows to test the following:

- The effect of colours next to each other.
- The effect of a dark and a light colour on size.
- A small and large pattern within the same figure shape.
- The effect of horizontal and vertical lines.
- How texture affects size.

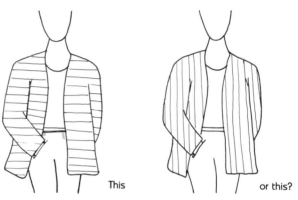

This   or this?

After each investigation draw conclusions and record your findings.

2. Colour wheel
Individual work (Investigation)

Make your own colour wheel using only the three primary colours. Work in the order suggested, primary colours first, secondary next and finally mix in the tertiaries to complete the circle.

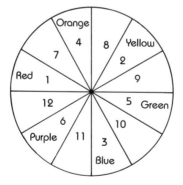

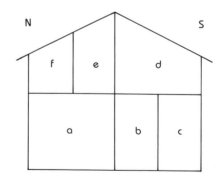

Use the completed colour circle to help you to suggest a range of colour schemes for the house illustrated which has:

- A sunless living room
- A small dining room
- A small, sunny kitchen
- A large bedroom
- A cold bathroom
- A small, dark nursery.

3. Colour consultation
Class work (Guest speaker and investigation)

Invite a colour consultant from a local store to talk to your class about wearing colours that suit people. Take part in the talk by volunteering to act as a model or host/hostess to welcome the speaker or to thank the speaker after the talk.

Follow up the talk by working in small groups using a range of scarves or pieces of coloured fabric to test against the faces of the people in your group to see which colours suit individuals best. Consider the person's skin tone, hair and eye colour. Make a list of recommended colours for each person in the group.

4. Personal image   Class work (Video and design)

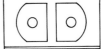

Watch the video *Textiles Studies* from programme 5 of the series, *Clothes Talk*. Comment on the choices of the fashion group.

Design your own outfit for a wedding disco. Give reasons for your choice of garment, fabric and colour. Display your design with others from your group in a class display.

5. Personalising clothing
Individual work (Design and investigation)

Design a motif for a T-shirt and investigate different ways of colouring the design. Evaluate each method and select one to use on an actual T-shirt.

When you have completed your design, test the market with others in your group and friends in school. If the result is favourable you could consider marketing the idea using the Young Enterprise Scheme.

6. Natural dyeing   Individual work (Investigation)

Choose one of the following substances to make a natural dye:

- Leaves
- Petals
- Berries
- Bark.

Collect some of your chosen material and make a dye solution by boiling the chopped substance in water and straining off the liquid. Use the dyestuff to test-dye different types of yarn such as wool, cotton, nylon, acrylic etc.

Bring the yarn to the boil in the dye solution and simmer for 30 minutes. Rinse it in cold water until the water is clear, dry it and then the yarn can be used for weaving, collage, embroidery, or on a display poster. An example is shown in the Appendices on page 52.

7. Badges   Individual work (Design and investigation)

A badge is another way of decorating your clothing in a personal way. Design a badge for yourself and investigate different ways of working the design in thread or fabric or of printing it onto fabric.

Evaluate each method and choose one method to use on a badge for a garment for yourself. Sketch the garment using the silhouettes provided if necessary.

Written work

Application of knowledge

Explain the difference between:

- Texture and pattern
- Complementary colours and harmonising colours
- Horizontal lines and vertical lines
- Tie-dyeing and tritik.

Problem solving

The instructions for dyeing a cotton T-shirt have been lost but there are sketches on the packet which illustrate the process. Explain the method shown using the pictures below and add advice on how a good result could be obtained.

Fact finding

Find out about the following people and their influence on textiles:

- William Henry Perkins
- Isaac Merrit Singer
- Ebeneezer Butterick
- Levi Strauss
- Charles MacKintosh.

Structured questions

1. All colours can be made from three primary colours, name them.

2. Give an example of a secondary colour and say how it is made.

3. Explain the terms:
   - tone • tint • shade.

4. Printing is a way of colouring fabric. Name two different ways of printing by hand and describe one in detail.

5. Your kitchen has a very sunny aspect; suggest a cool colour scheme for its decoration and give details of how the colours would be used.

6. How and why is colour used to improve the environment in which we live?

Data response

H O W T O M I C R O - D Y E

I N G R E D I E N T S

1 Pack of Hand Size (100g) Dylon Natural Fabric Dye

A microwave oven

A bowl suitable for use in a microwave – check there is still enough room for any turnable to rotate.

Plastic bag

Rubber gloves

Plastic spoon

1 pint of cold water

1 packet of Dylon Natural Fabric (Hand Size) is sufficient to Micro-Dye up to 250g (8oz) of cotton, polyester/cotton, linen or even silk.

The method is not suitable for wool or viscose and other synthetic fabrics. Remember that garments with metal, e.g. zips, studs, etc, must not be dyed in a microwave.

R E C I P E

We suggest you cover the working area with newspaper before you start.

1. Wash the fabric and leave damp (or wash and dry the fabric for a more definite pattern).

2. Wearing rubber gloves carefully tap the dye into the bowl and gradually add ½ pint of water. Stir thoroughly to make sure all the dye is dissolved – it may take a few minutes. Add the rest of the water.

3. Put the fabric into the bowl and work into the dye.

4. Cover the bowl with a plastic bag.

5. Put the bowl into the Microwave oven and set on 'High' for 4 minutes.

6. After 4 minutes, remove the bowl from the oven – remember to protect your hands from the heat.

7. Tip away the dye solution and rinse the fabric in cold water. To protect the pattern, do not undo any knots, twists, folds, etc until the first of the dye has been rinsed away.

8. When the water is running almost clear, wash the fabric in hot water with your normal wash powder to remove any remaining dye.

9. Dry away from direct heat and sunlight.

'colour is back!'

37

The information given describes a new method of fabric dyeing.

1   a) Which fibres are suitable for use with *Dylon Natural Fabric Dye®*?
    b) Which fibres are unsuitable?

2   How many packets of dye are needed to dye 500 g of cotton fabric?

3   Why must care be taken with metal fastenings in a microwave oven?

4   Draw five sketches to illustrate the method of micro-dyeing.

5   Explain the technique of knots, twists and folds which is mentioned in these instructions.

Free response

In the UK we traditionally associate weddings with the colour white and for funerals we wear black. Discuss the use of colour for special occasions and give other examples, e.g. sport and religious functions.

Self-assessment

Photocopy and complete the self-assessment chart on page 161, inserting the following list of topics under 'The work I have done includes':

1. Line
2. Pattern
3. Texture
4. Colour
5. Home dyeing – natural dyes
                 – commercial dyes
6. Resist dyeing techniques – tie-dye
                              – batik
                              – tritik
7. Hand printing
8. Embroidery – hand
              – machine.

Photocopy and complete the self-marking plan on page 162 for the seven working briefs in this unit.

Buying and making clothes

Core information ────────────

Study Area 1

Changes in shopping styles

Shopping has changed a great deal in recent years.

- Shops are larger and stock a wider variety of goods.
- There are fewer small family-run shops.
- Shopping centres are usually undercover with identical shops.
- Clothing can be bought in hypermarkets when food shopping.
- Hypermarkets cater for all types of shopping under one roof.
- Computerised shopping is frequently seen with bar code pricing, machine-readable tickets, kimball tags and magnetic tags.
- Teleshopping is a future development. Goods are ordered through a TV screen display using a hand held pad and pressing page numbers, sizes and colours.
- Catalogue ordering e.g. *Next Directory* has grown enormously.
- Designer goods are also now available by mail order and weekly payments.

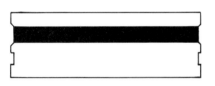

Magnetic tag

Bar code

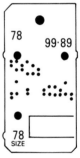

Machine-readable ticket

Budgeting and wardrobe planning

Budgeting for clothes means:

- Working out ahead how much you need to spend.
- Planning how you are going to save the money.
- Recording what you actually spend on items of clothing.
- Checking that you are keeping to the budget.
- Re-planning if your plan is not working.

Plan your wardrobe carefully by:

- Sorting out the clothes that you already have.
- Thinking about the types of occasions that you will need clothes for.
- Considering leisure, sport, school, work and special occasion outfits.
- Looking at the colours that you have and find basic accessories to match them.
- Taking the seasons of the year into account.

As the picture shows, a layered look is often more practical and can be used over a longer period of the year by adding or subtracting garments as the temperature changes. Co-ordinated separates can be very economical and by matching or contrasting colours and fabric textures different outfits can be created out of a few basic garments.

Add a few good accessories and you will expand your wardrobe possibilities and not be too hard up in the process.

Tips for accessories

- Keep accessories plain and in basic colours.
- Darker colours are easier to keep smart.
- Keep light shades clean.
- Good quality accessories can make a simple outfit look expensive.
- Use accessories with flair, for example the position of a brooch, a scarf tied in a special way, the shape of a bag or the angle of a hat will have more impact.

Storage and care of clothes

In order to keep your clothes looking smart:

- Store them well by hanging them or folding them flat.
- Keep them clean by removing stains and washing them regularly.
- Repair them as soon as they need it.
- Replace lost buttons, restitch hems.
- Dry clean those which need dry cleaning.
- Store clothes for winter or summer in a clean condition.
- Knitwear is best stored flat rather than hanging as it may stretch.
- Look at the care labels inside your clothes and care for them correctly.

Making your own clothes

Making your own clothes offers you the chance to be more individual as you will rarely see someone else wearing the same style, colour and fabric. The ability to make clothes will come with practice and you should not give up after your first attempt.

There are many advantages in making clothes:

- It generally works out cheaper than buying clothes.
- You can choose the colour, style and fabric.
- The garment should be the correct size and fit.
- It should be well made.
- You can be proud of having made it yourself.
- You can have more clothes for your money.

Original garments can be created by:

- designing your own styles
- making your own patterns
- adapting basic patterns to your own style.

This will take skill and practice, so learn to walk before you run by following the advice which follows.

Choosing a paper pattern

Paper patterns can be obtained from:

- counter catalogues in fabric departments and shops
- postal services offered in pattern magazines
- pull-out supplements in magazines.

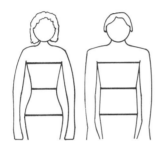

Pattern size depends on your basic measurements:

- chest/bust   • waist   • hips.

- Compare your basic measurements with those on the measurement chart.
- See which pattern size is the nearest to your measurements.
- Buy the nearest one to your measurements.

When you have bought the paper pattern you will find that there are probably different styles on the front of the envelope as well as the one which you chose. Each one is numbered with a view number.

- Decide which view number you are making.
- Look at the recommended fabrics on the back of the envelope.
- Find a fabric which you like and which is suitable.
- Ask what the fabric is made from.
- Ask how wide it is.

You now have all the facts to calculate how much fabric to buy.

Buy the fabric and the notions which you will need to make the garment. The notions are listed on the back of the pattern envelope.

Equipment and tools for sewing

In order to make your own clothes at home you will need:

- Cutting-out shears
- Small pointed scissors
- Tape measure
- Pins
- Needles
- Thread
- Sewing machine
- Iron and ironing board.

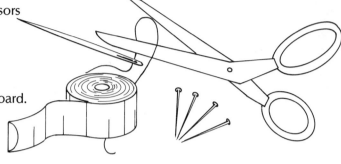

Irons

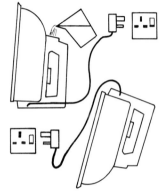

An iron should be cared for if it is to be kept in good condition.

- Check that it is electrically safe.
- Check the wires for fraying.
- Check the plug for cracks.
- Check the fuse for size.
- If it is used as a steam iron always stand it on end when it is not in use.
- Never fill it with water when it is plugged into the socket.
- When you have finished, empty out any remaining water.
- Store it in an upright position to prevent leaks.
- Keep the base of the iron clean and unscratched.
- Use the correct setting on the dial for the fabric being ironed.

  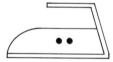 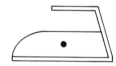

Hot (210 °C)
Cotton, linen,
viscose

Warm (160 °C)
Wool, polyester,
silk, mixtures

Cool (120 °C)
Nylon, acetate,
acrylic

Sewing machines

There are four main types of sewing machines on sale:

- basic machines such as the *Singer Samba*®
- electronically controlled machines such as the *Bernina Electronic*®
- programmable machines such as the *New Home Mystyle* computer model 826.
- overlock machines such as the *Husqvarna Huskylock*®.

Singer Samba

New Home

Bernina

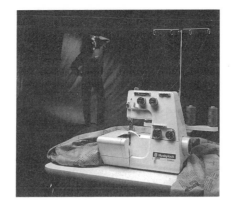

Husquarna Huskylock

Buying a new machine?

Ask yourself these questions:

- What do you want the machine to do?
- How much do you want to pay?
- Is the size and weight important?
- What extras are included with the machine?
- Is the machine noisy to use?
- Is there a guarantee and how long is it for?
- Is there an after-sales service?
- Are lessons available or will it be demonstrated?
- Do you need advanced technology or is a basic machine sufficient?

Caring for a sewing machine

A sewing machine will last longer and work more efficiently if you look after it. This can be done in the following ways:

- Keep it clean and free from dust and fluff under the teeth.
- Cover it or put it in its case when it is not in use.
- Use the correct spools and needles for the make of machine.
- Check that it is in good electrical order.
- Oil the moving parts regularly.
- Have it repaired and serviced professionally.
- Never force a machine when you are using it.

Additional equipment

The following equipment would also be useful for home sewing:

- Dress form
- Sleeve board
- Full length mirror
- Hem leveller
- Metre rule or yard stick
- Tracing wheel and carbon paper
- Stitch ripper
- Tailor's chalk.

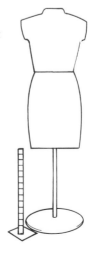

Ready-to-make kits

These are available from firms that produce catalogues of clothing and textile articles which are ready printed onto fabric for you to cut out. Some kits are already cut out for you and come with instructions for you to sew the articles up. *Clothkits®* is an example of ready-to-make clothing. This method of making clothes is helpful because:

● It avoids buying paper patterns.
● The fabric is chosen for you.
● The pieces are sometimes already cut out.
● Alternatively, the layout is done for you.
● The fabric amount has been calculated.
● There are written instructions to follow.
● The catalogue allows you to co-ordinate garments and colours.

Renovating clothes

Clothes can be renovated in order to save money or provide additional garments. Restyling and up-dating old clothes made from good fabric is easy to do and adult clothing can be used for children in this way. The illustration shows several ways of renovating an outfit for a young child:

● Add coloured turn-ups to short trousers.
● Cover a tear with a patch pocket.
● Lengthen the straps or fit new ones.
● Add a new T-shirt in a contrasting fabric.

Other ways of renovating garments are:

● lengthening with bands of coloured fabric   ● adding frills and edgings for length   ● making trousers into shorts   ● shortening sleeve lengths   ● adding new buttons, belts, cuffs or collars.

Pupil participation ────────

Working briefs

1. Shopping for clothes   Individual work (Investigation)

On a street map of your town draw in the different shops which sell items of clothing, e.g. supermarkets, chain stores, boutiques etc.

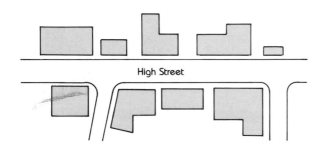

High Street

Look at your map and see if there is an area where clothes shops are near to each other. Can you explain the distribution of clothing shops?
Now answer these questions:

a) Which items of clothing are difficult to obtain in your town?
b) Where can you go for a special outfit?
c) Can a handicapped person get a wheelchair into shops in your town?
d) Does the town cater for all ages?

2. Buying clothes   Group work (Discussion)

Discuss the following aspects of buying clothes in small groups with a group leader to report the points raised to the class in the final summary discussion. The topics under discussion should include:

a) Methods of obtaining clothes.
b) Different types of shops where clothes can be obtained.
c) Priorities when choosing clothes.
d) Ways of paying for purchases.

3. Wardrobe planning and budgeting
Group work (Problem solving)

Jane is on a YTS scheme as a shop assistant for 12 months. She has the clothes that she had at school.

a) Pupil 1 – Plan a basic wardrobe for Jane for this year.
b) Pupil 2 – Cost the price of a new pair of shoes, a bag, an umbrella, a jacket and a waterproof garment.
c) Pupil 3 or 1 and 2 together – List the different ways that Jane could obtain clothes other than new ones as she has very little money to spend.

4. Storage of clothes
Individual work (Problem solving and computer program)

Draw a plan of your ideal modern fitted bedroom. Plan to include cupboards and units that would give you all types of storage. Give a written description

of the room and give reasons for your choice of everything included on the plan.

Alternatively use the computer program *Design A House*, Micro At Work, Software Pack 3.

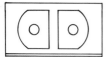

5. Paper pattern production   Class work (Video)

Watch the video *Fashion from Start to Finish* produced by Vogue Butterick Ltd.

Afterwards describe in your own words how a paper pattern is made.

6. Mail order catalogues   Class work (Survey)

a) Carry out a survey of mail order catalogues in use by your class group. Record which firms are used, type of goods bought and methods of payment.
b) Illustrate your findings on a chart or graph.
c) Collect advertisements from magazines for mail order catalogues. Study the incentives that are offered to new agents.
d) Use the software package *Mail Order*, Micro At Work No., 4. As a class you can create a mail order catalogue as a mini-enterprise package and buy and sell goods from it.

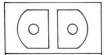

7. Sewing machines   Class work (Demonstration and video)

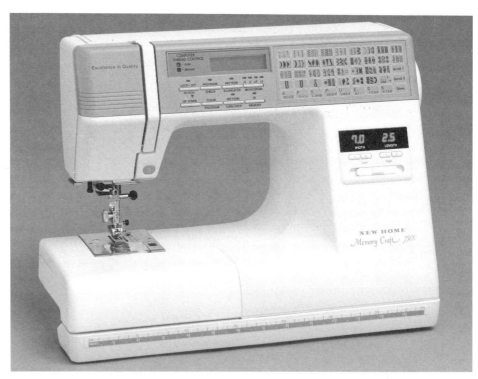

Arrange for a local sewing machine retailer to come into your school and demonstrate the latest models of computerised sewing machines.

Alternatively you could watch the video *Memorycraft 7500* produced by New Home® Machines Ltd.

After the demonstration or video, discuss the value of an expensive computerised machine for home sewing.

8. Buying fabric for home sewing
Individual work (Investigation)

Assess five samples of fabric for the following properties:
- thickness   ● weight   ● texture   ● closeness of weave
- drape   ● creasing.

Draw up a chart to summarise the results. Suggest a use for each fabric.

9. Accessories
Individual work (Design)

Accessories improve any basic outfit. Design a basic garment or outfit and
sketch a variety of accessories that could be worn with it to give a variety of
looks for different occasions. Suggest a colour scheme, fabrics and textures.

Written work

Fact finding exercise

Find out about and compare:

- Multi-sized paper patterns
- Easy-to-sew paper patterns
- Patterns sized for stretch knits only
- Overlock sewing patterns.

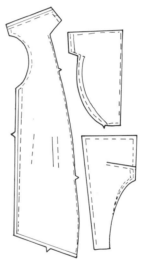

Application of knowledge

You have been given a workbox for Christmas and you are going to spend
your Christmas money on tools to put inside it.
List the tools that you will need and find out the cost of each item. How
much money will you need to spend?

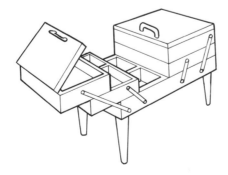

Give advice on how each item should be cared for so that it remains in good
condition.

Short answer questions

1. Which three basic measurements are needed to buy a paper pattern?

2. Name three fabric widths available in shops.

3. What type of needle is used for embroidery?

4. What is a 'primer'?

5. Where will you find a layout diagram?

6. What is meant by ● ● on the iron control?

7. Name two fibres which use this setting of the iron.

8. What are 'notions'?

9. Explain the term 'mix and match' separates.

10. What is meant by 'hire purchase'?

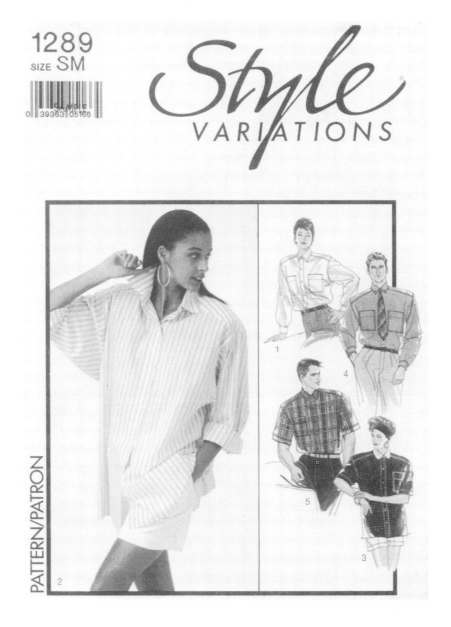

1289
SIZE SM

0 39363 05166

Style
VARIATIONS

PATTERN/PATRON

 1289 10 PIECES

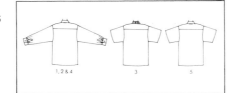

1, 2 & 4   3   5

Price code	U.S.A.	Canada
P	**$5.95**	**$7.95**

Misses' and Men's Shirt: Loose, straight shirt has shoulder yoke. Models 1, 2 and 4 have long, cuffed sleeves. Models 3 and 5 have short sleeves. Models 3 and 5 have one, and Models 1 and 4 have two breast pockets. Model 3 has purchased ribbed collar. **Suggested fabrics** – Broadcloth, challis, chambray, gingham, madras, shirtings. No allowance made for matching plaids, checks, stripes or large patterned fabrics. For fabric with nap, pile, shading or one-way design; use nap requirements and nap layouts. **To complete garment** – Thread, 0.60m (⅝yd) of 60 to 90cm (23" to 36") woven or non-woven interfacing. Models 1 and 2: Eight 1cm (⅜") buttons. Model 3: Six 1cm (⅜") buttons, one purchased collar. Model 4: Ten 1cm (⅜") buttons. Model 5: Six 1cm (⅜") buttons.

Size/Cms			X-Small 73.5–80	Small 81.5–86.5	Medium 89–92.5	Large 96.5–102	X-Large 107–112	
Mod. 1, 4	Shirt	115 cm*	2,50	2,50	2,50	2,80	2,90	Mtrs
	Chemise	150 cm***	1,70	1,80	1,90	2,00	2,10	"
Mod. 2	Shirt	115 cm**	2,30	2,40	2,50	2,70	2,80	Mtrs
	Chemise	150 cm**	1,70	1,80	1,80	2,00	2,10	"
Mod. 3	Shirt	115 cm*	2,00	2,10	2,10	2,20	2,40	Mtrs
	Chemise	150 cm*	1,40	1,60	1,60	1,70	1,70	"
Mod. 5	Shirt	115 cm**	2,10	2,20	2,20	2,50	2,60	Mtrs
	Chemise	150 cm**	1,40	1,60	1,60	1,70	1,80	"
Longeur de la chemise			78	79	81	82	83	Cms

*tissu sans sens,   **avec sens,   ***avec ou sans sens

Size/ Cms	X-Small Très Petite	Small Petite	Medium Moyenne	Large Grande	X-Large Très Grande
	73.5–80	81.5–86.5	89–92.5	96.5–102	107–112

Data response

From the information on the back of the pattern envelope answer the following questions:

1. a) How many views of the garment are illustrated?
    b) Which fabrics are suitable for the pattern?
    c) What types of fabric have not been allowed for?
    d) How much 115 cm width fabric is needed for medium size model 2 shirt?
    e) How much less fabric do you need to buy if the fabric is 150 cm wide?

2. Describe the style of model 4 shirt.

3. List the notions needed to complete model 3 shirt.

4. When buying fabric for the garment what tests can you carry out in the shop before buying the fabric?

5. Making clothes has many advantages over buying clothes. Discuss the advantages of home sewing and making your own clothes.

Problem solving

What advice would you offer to the following people in these situations:

1. You are out shopping with your friend and they see a jacket which is very up-to-date and they want to buy it.

2. It is the school disco at the end of term and you have nothing to wear that you have not worn before. Unfortunately you have only two weeks pocket money to spend and cannot afford to pay much.

3. Your sister has a room with little storage space for clothes and she is worried that nothing will be fit to wear.

Free response

A young mother can save money if she can make clothes for her children. Do you agree with this statement?
Suggest several ways in which she could renovate clothes that she already has for the children. Sketch one renovation and give details of how it could be done.

Self-assessment

Photocopy and complete the self-assessment chart on page 161, inserting the following list of topics under 'The work I have done includes':

1. Buying clothes
2. Budgeting and wardrobe planning
3. Storage and care of clothes
4. Making clothes
5. Equipment and tools for sewing
6. Using a paper pattern
7. Ready-to-make kits
8. Renovating clothes.

Photocopy and complete the self-marking plan on page 162 for the eight working briefs in this unit.

Appendices – Study Area 1

UNIT 1

Fashion interview

Prepare a questionnaire like the sample one given on the next page. Replies could be written down or recorded on tape. The people interviewed should be from a wide range of ages and both sexes. This will give a picture of fashion over a number of years.

FASHION QUESTIONNAIRE

Name ....

QUESTION	ANSWER
1. What clothes did you wear to school?	....
2. What did you wear on a Sunday?	....
3. Who chose your clothes?	....
4. Describe any special clothes that you can remember.	....
5. Did you ever wear a hat as a child?	....
6. Describe your wedding outfit.	....
7. What kind of swimwear can you remember wearing?	....
8. What clothes did you hate to wear as a child?	....
9. How many pairs of shoes did you have at a time?	....
10. Did you ever follow fashion trends? Which ones can you remember?	....

Video-Fashion Means Business

The following questions can be answered during or after the video has been watched.

1. Where are the British fashion shows held?

2. How often are they held?

3. Name a street in London which is famous for 'young' fashion.

4. Give reasons why pattern cutting is so important.

5. What is a 'toile'? Why is it made?

6. How can a designer protect original work from being copied?

7. What modifications to fashion are needed for Arab markets?

8. What does PR stand for? What does the job involve?

9. Do you think that it is easy to be a designer? If not, why not?

10. Do you agree with the title of the video? Give reasons why.

Unit 2

A figure comparison window

This is made as follows:

1. Cut two pieces of card 14 cm × 10 cm.

2. Draw a line down the centre of one piece of card to make two windows.

3. Sketch identical figure shapes in each half.

4. Cut out the shaded areas in each figure.

5. Fasten the two pieces of card together at the sides, base and centre line.

6. Prepare sample cards 6 cm × 11 cm of different colours, patterns, line and textured fabrics.

7. Use the windows to test the effect of different cards on the same figure proportions.

Natural dyeing

Summary poster

Collect together the information from each member of the class:

● plant used   ● sample of yarn dyed.

Arrange the samples under colour headings to show the range of colour.

Red	Blue	Yellow	Purple	Green	Orange	Brown	Black
Peony		Marigold		Moss		Onion	
				Privet		Tea	

Unit 3

Mail order catalogues

Survey results

The results of the survey of mail order catalogues can be shown in chart form as illustrated:

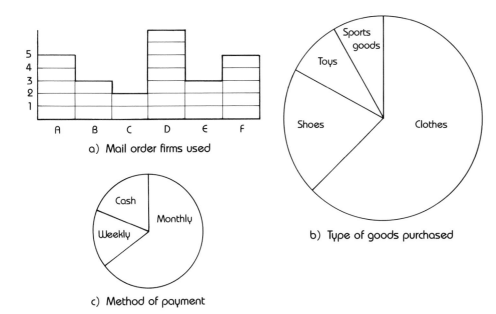

a) Mail order firms used

b) Type of goods purchased

c) Method of payment

Resources guide

Useful addresses

Simplicity and Style Patterns Ltd, PO Box 1, Blantyre, Glasgow, Scotland
McCall Pattern Distributors, PO Box 27, Athey Street, Macclesfield, Cheshire SK11 8EA
Butterick and Vogue Patterns, New Lane, Havant, Hampshire PO9 2ND
Pfaff Sewing Machines, Earl Street, Leeds LS9 8EH
New Home Sewing Machines, Cromwell Road, Bredbury, Stockport, Cheshire
Rowenta (UK), 9 The Street, Ashtead, Surrey
Dylon Dyes, Dylon International, London SE26 5HD
The Creative Textiles Group, 57 Rowsley Street, Leicester LE5 5JP

Books

Books	Publisher
The Dictionary of Costume, R. Turner Wilcox	Batsford
The Guinness Guide to 20th Century Fashion, D. Bond	Guinness
In Vogue, G. Howell	Penguin
McDowells Directory of 20th Century Fashion	Muller
A History of Fashion, Anderson Black, Garland Kennet	St. Michael
Handbook of Costume, J. Arnold	Macmillan

The History of Childrens' Costume, E. Ewing	Batsford
Basic Fashion Design, J. Ireland	Batsford
Fashion Design Drawing, J. Ireland	Batsford
Always In Style, D. Pooser	Piatkus
Dress for your Lifestyle, K. Samuel	St. Michael
ABC's of Fashion and Design, G. Mortimer Dunn	Foulsham
Colour Craft, J. Allen	Hamlyn
Colour Psychology and Colour Therapy, Birren	Citadel
Create your own Natural Dyes, K. Shultz	Sterling
Dyes from Natural Sources, A. Dyer	Bell & Hyman
The Creative Sewing Machine, A. Coleman	Batsford
The Complete Computer Sewing Book, M. Coles	Heinemann
The Sewing Machine Book, M. Coles	Hutchinson
Embroidery, M. Gostellow	Marshall Cavendish
Inspiration for Embroidery, C. Howard	Batsford
Mary Thomas' Dictionary of Embroidery Stitches	Hodder and Stoughton
Needlework School, Embroiderers Guild	Windward
The Art of Painting on Silk, 1, 2, P. Dawson	Search Press

Videos

BBC Textile Studies	BBC Enterprises Ltd. 80 Wood Lane, London.
Fashion Means Business	Design Council Educational, PO Box 10, Wetherby, Yorkshire.
Fashion From Start To Finish	Vogue Butterick Ltd. New Lane, Havant, Hampshire.
Memorycraft 7000 . . .	New Home Sewing Machines, Stockport, SK6 2SH
A Smart Move	ABLCRS, 7 Churchill Court, 58 Station Road, North Harrow, Middlesex, HA2 7SA

Software

FADS (Fashion Design and Figure Appreciation)	Advisory Unit, Endymion Road, Hatfield, Herts, AL10 8AU
Micro at Work, packs 3 and 4	GSN Educational Software 214 Stamford Street, Ashton-under-Lyne, Lancashire OL6 7LP

Teaching packs

Creative Textiles Group Basic Shapes, Texture, Colour, Personal Image	57 Rowsley Street, Leicester LE5 5JP
The Consumer File, Midland Bank	Forbes Publications

Textile technology

UNIT ONE

Fibres

Study Area **2**

Core information ————————————————

A fibre is:

● a hair-like structure ● a short staple length or a continuous filament length ● natural or man-made.

Fibres which occur naturally are obtained chiefly from animals and plants.

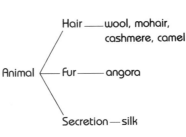

Animal ⟨ Hair —— wool, mohair, cashmere, camel

Fur —— angora

Secretion — silk

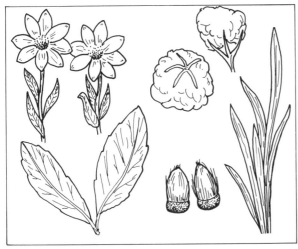

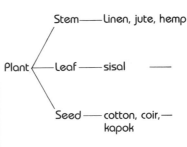

Plant ⟨ Stem —— Linen, jute, hemp

Leaf —— sisal

Seed —— cotton, coir,— kapok

Animal fibres

Wool

Wool is the most important animal fibre and the quality of the wool depends upon the breed of sheep and where they are reared. Merino sheep produce the best quality wool and they are reared mainly in Australia.

The picture shows the thick coat of the Merino sheep which can weigh as much as 6.4 kg. The wool is excellent quality being fine and soft and is used for high-quality woollen and worsted fabrics.

Wool is used for:

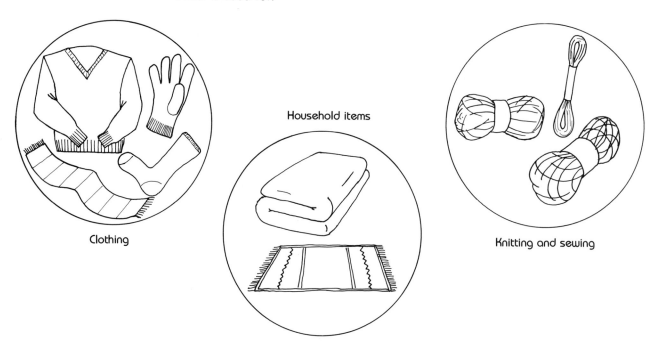

Clothing

Household items

Knitting and sewing

 Woollen items can carry two special labels issued by the International Wool Secretariat.

The Woolmark is given to items which are made from 100 % pure new wool.

 The Woolblendmark, also called woolrichblend, is given to items which have at least 60 % pure new wool in the blend.

Wool need not be new wool when it is used to make fabric. Wool can be recycled, having been made into shoddy from old garments.

Items can carry labels which show the country of manufacture such as the British Wool label illustrated.

Other breeds of sheep include Romney, Corriedale, South Down and Leicester. The wool from these breeds is coarser but equally valuable for the woollen industry. The coarsest wools often come from mountain sheep and they are famous for Shetland wool and Harris Tweed.

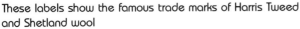

These labels show the famous trade marks of Harris Tweed and Shetland wool

Sheep are sheared once a year and the fleece is removed in one piece and taken away for processing. Processing consists of:

- Cleaning – removing the dirt and grease.
- Carbonising – removing twigs, leaves etc.
- Carding – straightening the fibres by brushing them.
- Combing – for worsteds only, an extra combing to remove tangles.
- Spinning – twisting the fibres together to make yarn.

Wool is:
- warm
- absorbent
- elastic
- resistant to burning
- showerproof
- open to attack by moths
- likely to shrink unless treated
- not strong.

If you look at a wool fibre under a microscope it will look like this:

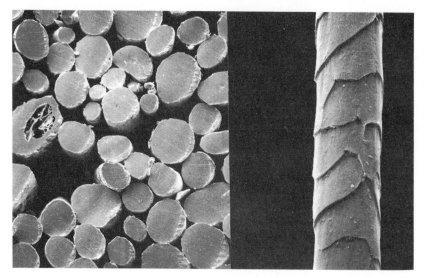

Wool

Notice the scales on the wool fibre overlapping each other and having points at the edges.

Silk

Silk comes from the cocoon of the silk moth (*Bombyx mori*) which is farmed (sericulture) for its silk.

There is a two month cycle in the production of silk:

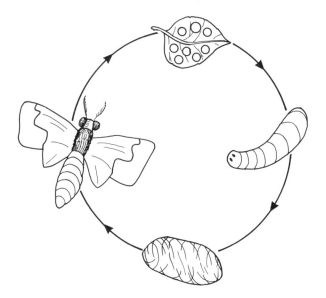

- The moth lays its eggs.
- The hatched grubs start to feed.
- They grow quickly and shed four skins.
- After 35 days they start to spin a cocoon.
- The silk comes from two holes (spinnerets) in the top of the head.
- Inside the cocoon they turn into a moth.
- The moth emerges and the cycle begins again.

When silk is farmed the moth is not allowed to break out of the cocoon as it damages the silk threads. Instead the chrysalis is killed before it emerges and the silk can then be wound off in a continuous filament. The miscroscope views of silk show the smooth glass-like fibres which can be 1 mile (1.6 km) in length.

Silk

Silk is processed in the following way:

● Reeling – unwinding the cocoons to obtain the silk.
● Throwing – twisting the filaments.
● Spinning – twisting the thrown silk.
● De-gumming – removing the stiff gum.

Silk is:

● very strong   ● elastic   ● warm   ● absorbent   ● smooth
● flammable   ● easily damaged   ● expensive.

The Silk mark illustrated is used on pure silk fabrics and items made from 100% silk.

Silk is used for:

Clothing

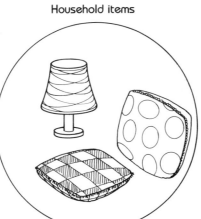

Household items

Threads and cords

Other animal fibres

Fibre	Mohair	Cashmere	Camel hair	Angora
Obtained from:	Goat	Goat	Bactrian camel	Rabbit
Used for:	Knitwear Fabric blends	Expensive knitwear Fabric blends	Coatings	Knitwear Fabric blends

Plant fibres

Linen

Linen comes from the flax plant (*Linum*) which grows in damp conditions. It is grown as an annual crop in Ireland, Belgium and France and has blue flowers. The stem is important for the fibres as flax is a bast fibre and the plant is harvested so that the whole stem is pulled and not cut. The microscope sections show this woody, rather bamboo-like structure.

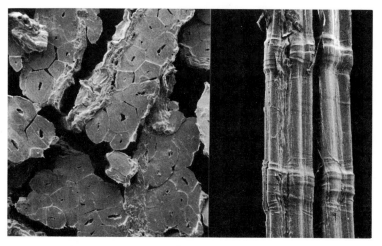

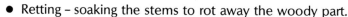
Linen

The processing of flax to produce linen is:

- Retting – soaking the stems to rot away the woody part.
- Scutching – breaking the stems without damaging the fibres.
- Hackling – combing the fibres.
- Carding – straightening the fibres into parallel lines.
- Spinning – twisting the fibres to make yarn.

The Linen logo is used to mark fabrics and items which are 100% pure linen and different countries have their own symbols to show origin such as the Irish linen mark.

Linen is:

- strong wet and dry • cool to wear • absorbent • durable
- bleachable • hardwearing • flammable • creasable • affected by mildew.

Linen is used for:

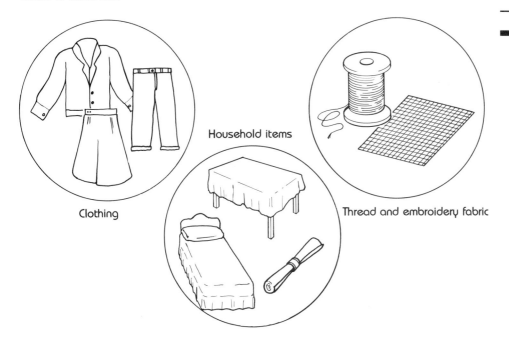

Clothing

Household items

Thread and embroidery fabric

Cotton

Cotton is the most important plant fibre grown in the world. It is a seed fibre of the cotton plant which is grown as a crop in the USA, India, Egypt, the West Indies and other countries. The seed is sown in the spring and the plants develop white flowers which become seed bolls. The fibres grow inside the boll which bursts open when it is ripe. The cotton is picked and processing begins:

- Ginning – to remove the seeds.
- Grading – to ascertain the quality of fibre.
- Baling – for transporting the cotton to the mills.
- Cleaning – to remove dirt and leaves.
- Carding – the brushing and straightening of the fibres.
- Combing – high quality cottons require extra combing.
- Drawing – straightening the slivers.
- Spinning – the roving is stretched and twisted.

The twisted nature of the cotton fibre is seen under the microscope.

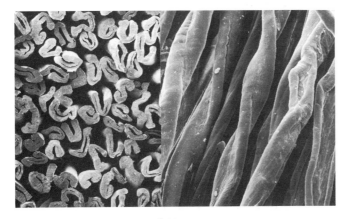

Cotton

Cotton is:

- strong, wet and dry
- resistant to chemicals
- affected by mildew
- cool to wear
- washable
- creasable.
- absorbent
- bleachable
- healthy
- flammable

Cotton is used for:

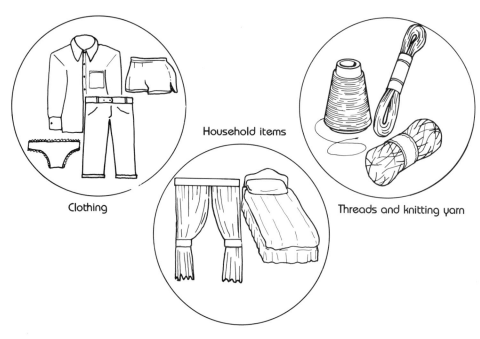

Clothing

Household items

Threads and knitting yarn

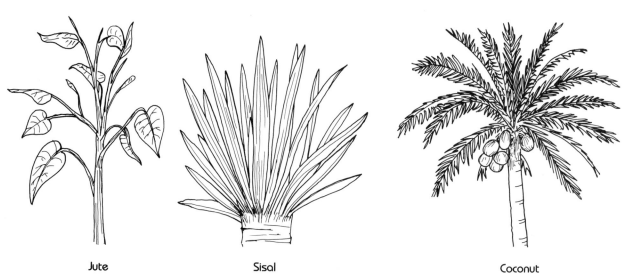

Jute

Sisal

Coconut

Other plant fibres

Fibre	Jute	Hemp	Sisal	Coir	Kapok
Obtained from:	Stems	Stems	Leaves	Coconut shells	Seeds
Used for:	Sacking Carpets	Rope String	Matting Cord	Matting	Stuffing

Man-made fibres

People first got the idea of making fibres from watching the silk worm spinning liquid filaments of silk through holes in its head. If they could make a fibre-forming liquid and sieve it through a spinneret then they too could make filament fibres or artificial silk.

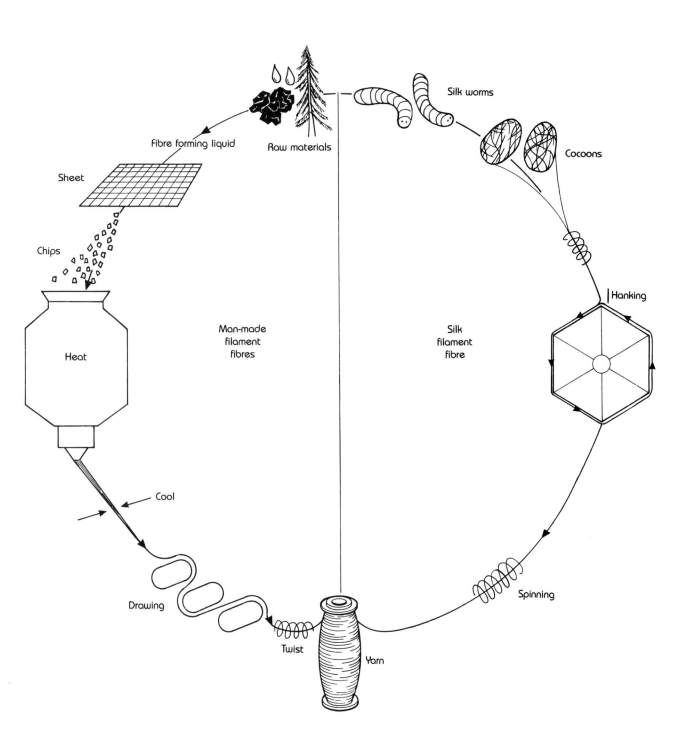

Fibre forming liquid

Raw materials

Silk worms

Sheet

Cocoons

Chips

Hanking

Heat

Man-made filament fibres

Silk filament fibre

Cool

Drawing

Spinning

Twist

Yarn

Looking through a microscope at man-made fibres it will be seen that they look very similar in long section to silk. It is only when they are seen in cross section that the differences are apparent.

Viscose

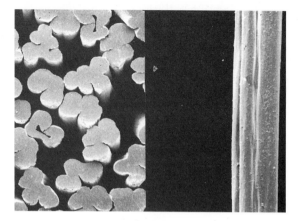

Acetate

Nylon

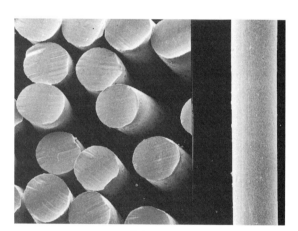

Polyester

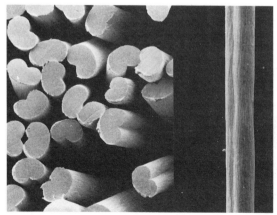

Acrylic

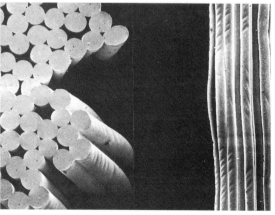

Lycra

Facts

- Artificial silk was developed at the end of the 19th century.
- It was called viscose in 1892.
- Acetate was first used as varnish on aircraft wings during World War I.
- It was called celanese in 1921.
- The discovery of nylon in 1938 gave us nylon stockings and parachutes during World War II.
- Polyester was developed in 1941 and ICI called it *Terylene*®
- Acrylic was developed after the war in America. *Acrilan*® arrived in 1952.
- Lycra was discovered in 1958 as the first elastane fibre.

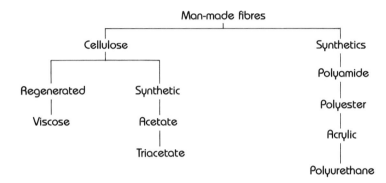

The fibre names used on the chart are **generic** names indicating the family name of each group of fibres. Manufacturers also use a trade name for their product to distinguish it from other fibres of the same type. It is helpful to be able to identify these trade names to know what fibre you are actually buying. Below is a list of current trade names.

Generic name	Trade name
Viscose	*Vincel*®, *Sarille*®, *Evlan*®, *Fibro*®, *Viloft*®
Acetate	*Dicel*®, *Lansil*®
Triacetate	*Tricel*®, *Arnel*®, *Rhonel*®
Polyamide	*Nylon*®, *Bri-nylon*®, *Celon*®, *Enkalon*®, *Tactel*®
Polyester	*Terylene*®, *Trevira*®, *Dacron*®, *Lirelle*®
Acrylic	*Orlon*®, *Acrilan*®, *Courtelle*®, *Dralon*®
Polyurethane	*Lycra*®, *Spandex*®
PVC	*Rhovyl*®, *Vinyon*®, *Thermovyl*®
Polypropylene	*Courlene*®, *Cournova*®, *Ulstron*®, *Meraklon*®

Man-made fibres are produced in similar ways and the flow chart shows the basic processing common to all man-made fibres.

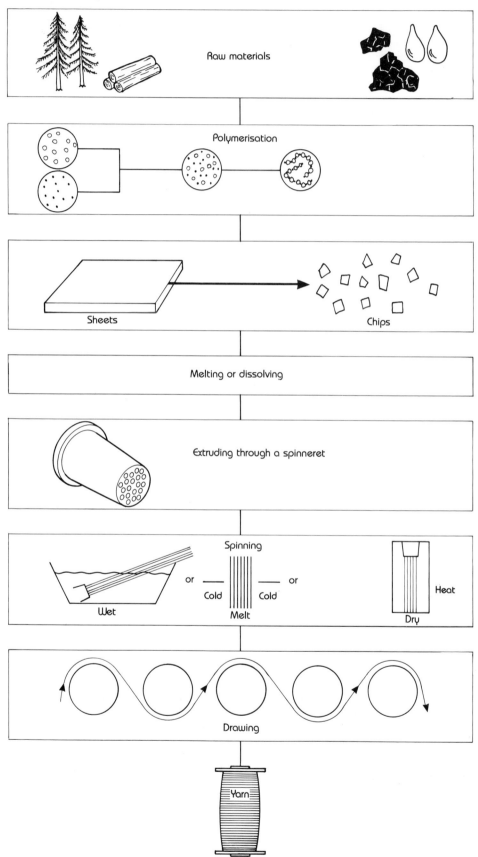

Raw materials

Polymerisation

Sheets   Chips

Melting or dissolving

Extruding through a spinneret

Spinning

Wet   or   Cold | Cold   or   Heat
              Melt   Dry

Drawing

Yarn

Although man-made fibres are made in a similar way the resulting fibres differ from one another in their properties and uses.

	Viscose	Acetate	Polyamide	Polyester	Acrylic	Elastane
Strength	**	**	****	****	***	**
Absorbency	****	***	**	**	*	*
Warmth	**	*	*	**	**	*
Elasticity	*	**	***	***	***	****
Flammability	****	****	**	**	***	*
Crease resist	*	**	***	****	***	****

	Viscose	Acetate	Polyamide	Polyester	Acrylic	Elastane
Uses						

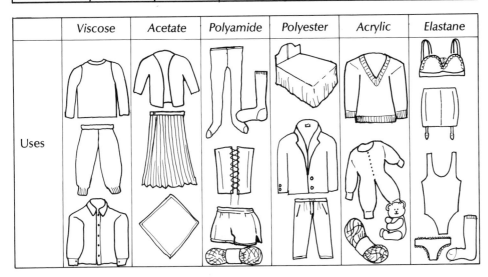

Facts

- All man-made fibres are filament fibres.
- They can be cut into staple lengths and spun into a yarn.
- Man-made fibres can be substitutes for natural fibres, e.g. acrylic is a wool substitute, viscose imitates cotton.
- The only flame-resistant fibres are modacrylic, glassfibre and asbestos.
- Most man-made fibres are thermoplastic and can be heat-set (pleated).
- Viscose is not thermoplastic.
- Elastane fibres are used with other fibres (mixed-fibre fabrics).

Mixtures and blends

A mixture fabric is made from two or more different fibres e.g. warp in one fibre and weft in a different one. A union fabric is made in this way, linen union is made from cotton and linen and is used for tea-towels.

A blended fabric is made from fibres which have been blended together before spinning. *Viyella®* fabric is an example of a blended fabric of wool and cotton, as is seen on the label.
There are three reasons for mixing and blending:

- An improvement can be made to the properties of the fabric.
- A saving is made in cost by mixing an expensive fibre with a cheaper one.
- A fabric which has a texture or effect can be created e.g. wool and mohair.

> **VIYELLA**
> 55% wool 45% cotton

World fibre use

Although there has been an increase in demand for man-made fibres in recent years, natural fibres are still more popular and cotton leads all fibre production figures. Polyester is the most popular man-made fibre.

Fibre	1982	1983	1984	1985	1986	%
Natural	16417	16753	17255	18350	18921	54
Man-made	13091	14145	14942	15590	16098	46

World wide demand for fibres (in thousand metric tons) Textile Organon 1987

Pupil-participation

Working briefs

1. Microscope identification   Individual work (Investigation)

Investigate the appearance of fibres under a microscope either by using prepared slides or making your own as described on page 100.

Compare what you see with the pictures of fibres in this unit. Draw up a record chart to include a sketch of the fibre and its identity.

2. Fibre identification by burning
Individual work (Investigation)

Burning a fibre is another way of identifying it. You will need:
- a flameproof mat or tray   • tweezers or tongs   • a Bunsen burner or a candle and matches   • a bowl of water.

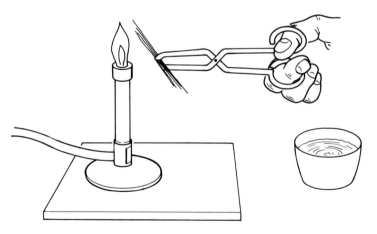

Take great care when carrying out the investigation. Observe carefully five things:

- a reaction to the flame approaching   • how it burns   • what happens when the flame is removed   • the smell   • what is left when the burning stops.

Compare what you observe with the chart and this should tell you the identity of the fibre.

Fibre	Approach	In Flame	Out of Flame	Smell	Residue
Wool	Slow to burn	Smoulders	Goes out	Burnt meat	Soft ash
Silk	Slow to burn	Burns slowly	Goes out	Burnt hair	Bulbous ash
Cotton	Catches fire	Burns quickly	Continues	Burning paper	Afterglow and grey ash
Linen	Catches fire	Flares quickly	Continues	Burning paper	Afterglow and a lot of ash
Viscose	Catches fire	Burns rapidly	Continues	Burning paper	Afterglow and black ash
Acetate	Catches fire	Burns rapidly	Continues	Hot vinegar	Brittle bead
Polyamide	Shrinks	Melts and drips	Goes out	Characteristic	Stringy bead
Polyester	Shrinks	Burns and melts	Goes out	Characteristic	Hard brown bead
Acrylic	Catches fire	Burns rapidly	Flares and smokes	Choking	Ashy bead

3. Fibre identification by dyeing
Group work (Investigation)

- Use a multi-fibre strip or individual pieces of white fabric of each fibre type.
- *Shirlastain A®* dye is the quickest and easiest to use.
- Place the strip or fabrics into the dye for a few minutes.
- Remove and rinse in cold water.
- Dry and observe the colour of the fabrics. Check the result against the chart below.

Wool	Silk	Cotton	Linen	Viscose	Acetate	Polyamide	Polyester	Acrylic
Golden yellow	Orange	Lavender	Violet blue	Pink	Greenish yellow	Dull yellow	Undyed	Pinkish grey

4. Fibre identification using chemicals
Group work (Investigation)

There are tests which identify a fibre by using chemicals. These tests are described on page 101 in the Appendices but when conducting any of these tests great care must be taken and a few simple rules should be followed:

- Handle chemicals with caution.
- Avoid spills and wipe up any which occur.
- Wear protective clothing, use gloves, goggles and an overall.
- Replace bottle stoppers after use.
- Store chemicals in a safe place.
- Dispose of chemicals carefully.

5. Natural fibre properties   Individual work (Discussion)

Look at the chart of man-made fibre properties on page 67 and draw up a similar one for natural fibre properties from the information in the unit.

Follow up by discussing the star ratings you decided upon with your group and agree on a final group chart for natural fibres.

6. Metallic fibres   Individual work (Design)

Metallic fibres are often used for decorative purposes in ceremonial dress. Sketch a garment which uses metallic yarns for decoration and plan part of the decoration in detail.

7. Using animals for clothing   Class work (Debate)

'Animals should not be used for clothing'.
Make a list of points agreeing with this statement and a second list which disagrees with it. Volunteer to speak in class in a debate which puts forward both sides of the argument.

Written work

Fact finding exercise

Ten important countries for fibre production are marked on the map of the world. Identify the countries and say which fibre each is important for.

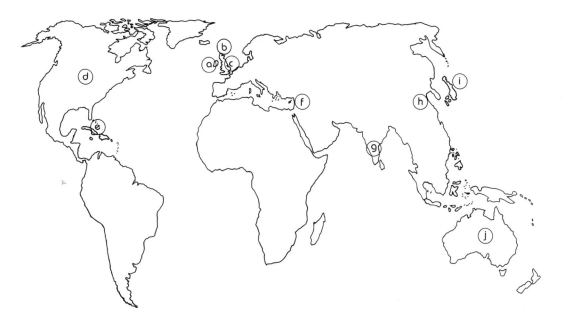

Application of knowledge

1. Complete the chart by putting the following fibres under the correct heading:
Acetate, Acrylic, Angora, Cashmere, Cotton, Glassfibre, Hemp, Jute, Linen, Mohair, Polyamide, Polyester, Silk, Viscose, Wool.

Natural	Regenerated	Synthetic

2. Explain the term 'regenerated' fibre.

Application of knowledge

School sock survey

A class survey of socks worn in summer revealed the results shown.

1. Give reasons why cotton and nylon was the most popular fibre mixture.

2. Explain why nylon on its own was the least popular.

3. Give reasons why pure cotton did not come top of the list.

4. Winter socks would include some different fibres. Suggest three that could be used for winter socks giving reasons for your choice.

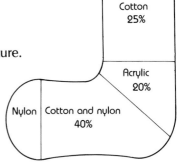

Cotton 25%

Acrylic 20%

Nylon | Cotton and nylon 40%

Problem solving

1. Mrs Brown is a frail old lady who has difficulty in keeping warm in the winter. What would you advise her to wear so that she does not lose body heat too quickly?

2. Mr Smith needs to economise on heating bills this winter. Suggest how insulating his house might help to do this.

3. Peter belongs to the cross-country team at school. His sports gear gets very dirty and needs to be washed frequently. What fibres would you advise him to look for when he buys a new running top?

4. Philip is allergic to wool and comes out in rashes if he wears it. He needs a new warm sweater for Christmas and he asks you to knit one. What yarns could you use?

5. Jane is getting married but cannot spend a lot of money on a dress. What do you advise?

Application of knowledge

1. Using the information in the chart on page 67, select a fibre for each of the items listed and give three reasons in each case for your choice.
   a) A cycle top
   b) A climbing rope
   c) A boat sail
   d) Kitchen curtains

2. The following labels were found on certain items of clothing. Sketch the items and give three reasons in each case for your choice.

1.   2.   3.  4.

Free response

Although man-made fibres are easy to care for, there is a preference for natural fibres as shown by the trade figures on page 68. Explain the attraction of natural fibres for clothing and household items and the rejection of easy-care man-made ones by many people.

Self-assessment

Photocopy and complete the self-assessment chart on page 161, inserting the following list of topics under 'The work I have done includes':

1. Natural fibres – wool
                    – silk
                    – linen
                    – cotton
2. Man-made fibres
3. Mixtures and blends
4. World fibre use.

Photocopy and complete the self marking plan on page 162 for the seven working briefs in this unit.

Yarns and fabrics

Core information ————————————————

Spinning

Spinning is:

- The process of producing filaments for man-made fibres.
- The twisting of staple fibres together to make yarn.

Spinning includes:

- cleaning
- carding
- drawing.

- Cleaning removes dirt and waste matter in staple fibres.
- Carding untangles the fibres and brushes them parallel.
- Drawing thins staple fibres into a strand for spinning.
- Drawing stretches man-made fibres and makes them stronger.

Spinning can be done by hand or machine.

All three methods put regular twist into the fibres and make them into yarn.

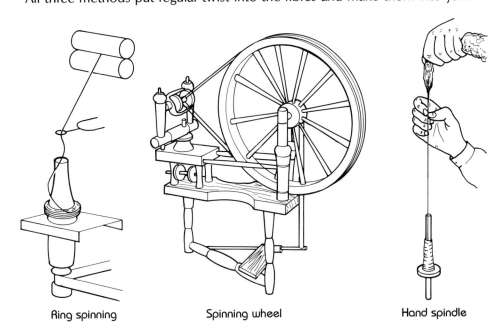

Ring spinning   Spinning wheel   Hand spindle

Yarn twist

Twist can be of two types:

- Z Twist = clockwise twist
- S Twist = anti-clockwise twist

The diagram shows how the names originated.

Yarn can also be:

- very tightly twisted
- tightly twisted
- moderately twisted
- slightly twisted.

The amount of twist decides what type of yarn is made.

Types of yarn

Yarns can be:

- single
- plied or folded
- cabled or corded.

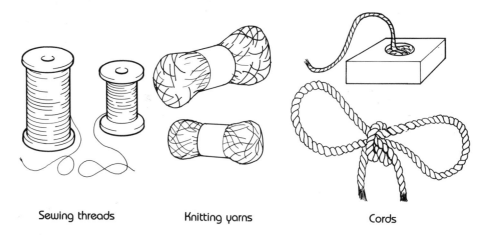

The illustration shows all three types:

Sewing threads   Knitting yarns   Cords

Thickness of yarn

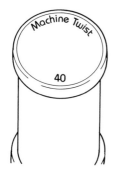

The thickness of sewing threads is shown by a numbering system called the cotton count. The numbers 30, 40 and 50 can be found on cotton thread such as those illustrated. The lower the number, the thicker the thread. Machine embroidery cotton is 30, normal sewing cotton is 40 and a fine cotton thread is 50 thickness.

Man-made yarns are measured in **denier**. The opposite rule applies here, the lower the number, the finer the thread e.g. 15 denier nylon tights are finer than 40 denier ones.

Textured yarns

A straight filament yarn can be softened and moulded into loops, folds, waves etc. The chart shows the various ways in which this is done to make textured man-made yarns.

Method	Effect	Trade name	Garment
False twist Stuffer box Edge crimping Knit-de-knit Air texturing		Helenca® Banlon® Agilon® Buclon® Taslon®	Stretch wear Underwear Stockings Knitwear Woven fabric

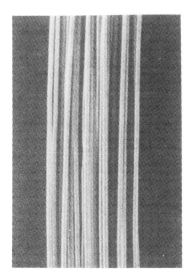

Before texturing

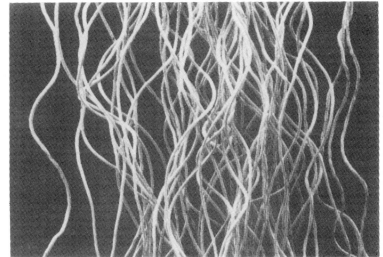

After texturing

Textured yarn is:

● more elastic   ● bulkier   ● warmer   ● interesting in appearance.

Novelty yarns

These are made from three yarns:

● a base yarn   ● an effect yarn   ● a tie yarn.

The diagram shows the three yarns twisted together. They can be self or multi-coloured.

Novelty yarns are interesting for their appearance, texture and colour effects.

The chart shows a variety of novelty yarns in production.

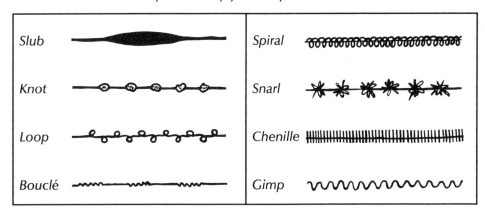

75

Fabric construction

There are three main ways of making fabric:

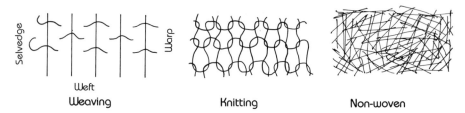

Weaving is:

- similar to darning
- interlacing two sets of threads (warp and weft)
- carried out on a loom.

How a loom works

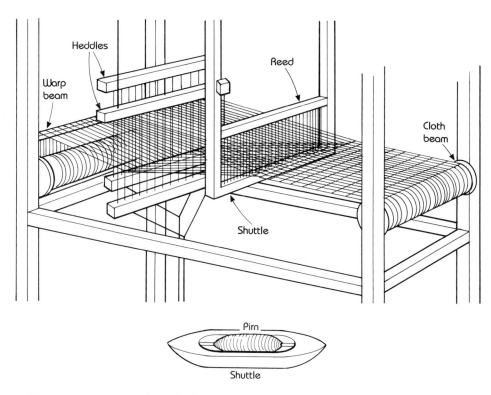

- The warp yarns are threaded from the warp beam, through the heddles and then through the reed to be fastened round the cloth beam.
- The weft yarns are wound onto a pirn which fits into a boat-shaped shuttle.
- The heddle lifts some warp threads to make a shed through which the shuttle passes.
- The reed beats the weft yarn into place.
- Another heddle lifts other warp threads and makes a new shed for the shuttle to return through.
- The selvedge is made at the sides by the turning of the shuttle.

Weaves

The pattern made by the interlacing of the two sets of threads is called the weave. There are three main weaves:

- plain weave   • twill weave   • satin weave.

Plain weave (also called tabby weave)

This is the simplest of all weaves:

- The yarn passes over and under alternate threads.
- Two rows form the pattern.

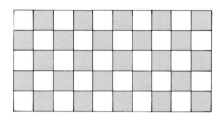

Examples of plain weave fabrics: calico, hessian, lawn, muslin.
Variations of a plain weave: basket or hopsack, haircord, rib.

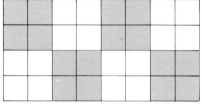
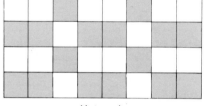
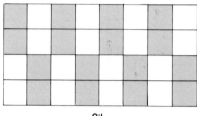

| Basket | Haircord | Rib |

Twill weave

This is recognised by diagonal lines across the fabric:

- The yarn passes over two and under two warp threads across a row.
- The order moves one thread to the left on the next row.
- Similarly on the third and fourth rows.
- Four rows form the pattern.

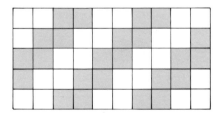

Examples of twill weave fabrics: denim, gaberdine, twill, tweed.
Variations on a twill weave: herringbone, chevron.

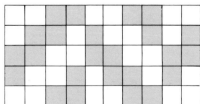
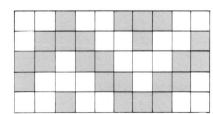

| Herringbone | Chevron |

Satin weave

This is noted for its shiny right side:

- Long warp threads lie across the surface.
- The weft passes over five or eight threads at a time.
- Five rows or eight rows form the pattern.

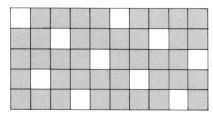

five end satin

Examples of satin weave fabrics: slipper satin, duchess satin, lining satin.

Variation on a satin weave: sateen

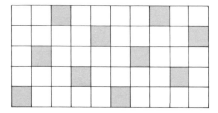

five end sateen

Other weaves

More complicated weaves can be worked on different looms, e.g. dobby and jacquard. Elaborate fabrics can be woven, e.g. brocade and damask. Pile weaves can produce fabric with a raised surface which can be cut or left looped.

Examples of pile fabrics: towelling, velvet, corduroy, needlecord.

Modern weaving methods

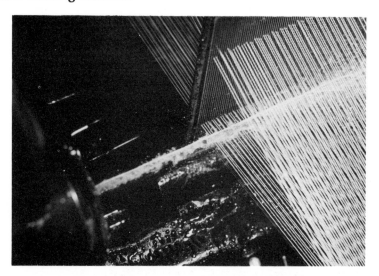

In this type of weaving the weft is carried across in a water jet. There are also air jet weaving machines which project the yarn across the warp yarns.

Knitting

Knitting is:

- yarn looped through other loops to make fabric
- worked by hand on needles
- worked by a machine which is flatbed or circular.

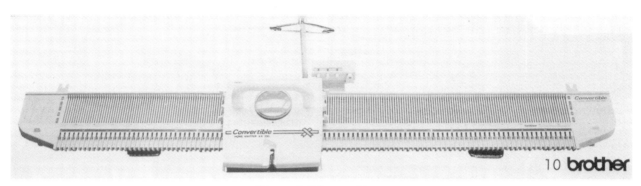

A home knitting machine

Hand knitting

A circular knitting machine

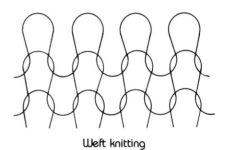

Weft knitting

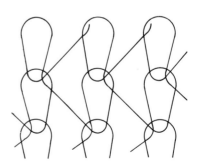

Warp knitting

There are two types of knitting:

- Weft knitting in which a single yarn moves across a row or course.
- Warp knitting in which many yarns run up the fabric, one to each column or wale.

Facts

- Knitting machines can do both warp and weft knitting. Most industrial machines are circular machines producing tubular lengths of fabric which have to be cut in order to be processed. They have no selvedges but the edges of the knitting are often sealed with sealant to allow it to be stentered at a later stage.
- Flatbed machines produce flat widths of fabric and they can shape or fashion garments to different sizes or shapes.
- There are two basic stitches from which all patterns are made: knit which is a flat stitch with a smooth surface and purl which is a bumpy stitch, the reverse of knit.
- Rib stitch is a combination of knit and purl. It gives an elastic effect and is used for cuffs, necklines and lower edges where fit is needed.
- Warp and weft knitted fabrics have different properties:

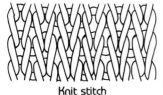

Knit stitch

Purl stitch

Rib stitch

Weft knit fabric	Warp knit fabric
Easy to unravel	Difficult to unravel
Ladders and runs if cut or pulled	Does not ladder or run
Curls at the edges when cut	Lies flat when cut
Very stretchy	Elastic but stable
Looses shape easily	Keeps its shape well
Has a right and wrong side	Both sides are the same
Examples:	Examples:
Jersey	Tricot
Interlock	Locknit
Stockinette	Raschel

Knitted fabrics are:

- warm to wear
- absorbent
- comfortable
- flexible
- crease shedding.

Non-woven fabrics or bonded fibre fabrics

New technology has made it possible to make fabrics from fibres without going through the yarn process. The fibres are bonded together by:

- using adhesives to stick the fibres together
- fusing thermoplastic fibres together with heat
- stitching a web of fibres together
- punching a web of fibres with needles.

Bonded fibre fabrics are used for:

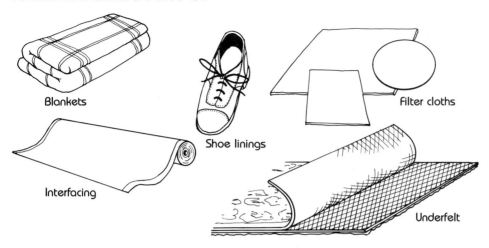

Blankets

Shoe linings

Filter cloths

Interfacing

Underfelt

Bonded fabrics are generally:

- stiffer than other fabrics ● shape retaining ● lacking drape and flexibility ● cheaper to produce and buy ● economical to cut as there is no straight grain ● useful for special purposes only as in disposable clothing etc.

Laminated fabrics

These consist of two or more fabrics stuck together in layers like a sandwich. Foam is often used to do this and it provides an insulating layer between the outer fabrics.

Laminated fabric is:

- warmer and thicker than other cloth ● stiffer and less drapable
- stronger than a single layer ● a double fabric needing no lining.

Laminated fabric is used for: coats, jackets, curtains, mattress covers.

Stretch fabrics

Rubber was the first stretch fabric but modern synthetic stretch yarns are far superior as they last longer and are finer. They are mixed into other fibres to make cloth such as swimwear fabrics, stockings and sportswear.

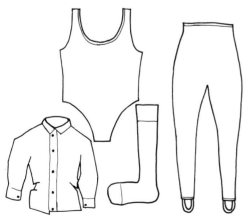

St Michael

WITH ELASTANE TO
RETAIN SHAPE

MARKS & SPENCER
·QUALITY CHILDRENSWEAR·

St Michael

COTTON
AND
ELASTANE

The fabric used in this
garment gives a fabulous fit
and keeps its shape as you
move.

Felting

This is one of the oldest methods of making fabric. The fibres of wool felt together when treated with moisture, heat and pressure. The cloth has a thick matted appearance and as it has no straight grain, it does not fray when cut.

As it can be moulded and shaped it has been used a great deal for hats. Other uses include: toy making, craft work and carpet underfelts.

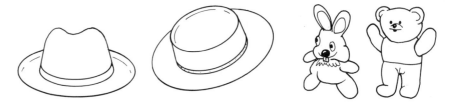

Net and lace

Both of these fabrics are made by the twisting of threads around each other to form mesh patterns. It can be done by hand or machine.
Netting can be used for:

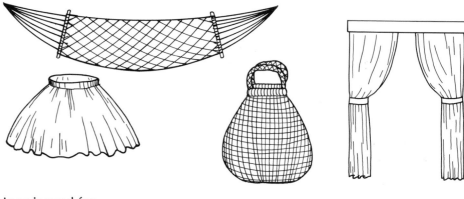

Lace is used for:

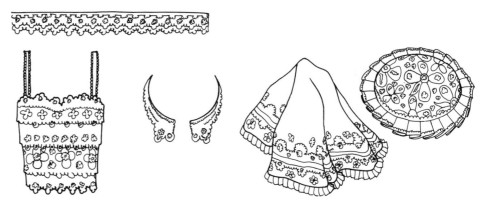

Fabric names

Most fabrics were given their names when they were first made from natural fibres. The names came from various sources:

● Towns where they were made, e.g. Bedford cord, Oxford cloth.
● Descriptions of the fabric itself, e.g. broadcloth, needlecord.
● The use to which they were put, e.g. cavalry twill, jean.
● The weave that was used, e.g. satin, twill.

With the development of man-made fibres the old names continued to be used as the man-made fabric was often copying the traditional natural fabric, e.g. polyester satin, nylon chiffon.

The glossary which follows describes the original fabric rather than the man-made fabric of the same name.

Glossary of fabrics

Aertex – A cellular cotton used for underwear and sportswear.
Bedford cord – A strong ribbed cotton, wool or mixture fabric.
Boucle – A curled surface effect wool.
Broadcloth – A wide good quality wool with a milled finish.
Broderie anglaise – An embroidered cotton with an eyelet decoration.
Brocade – A highly decorated jacquard fabric of silk, cotton or man-made fibre.
Calico – A cheap plain woven cotton, bleached or unbleached.
Cambric – A soft woven bleached cotton from Cambrai in France.
Cavalry twill – A strong twill weave cotton, wool or rayon.
Chambray – A two coloured fabric, with a white weft and a coloured warp of cotton.
Chenille – A tufted fabric of cotton, silk or wool.
Chiffon – A sheer fabric of silk or cotton.
Chino – A twill cotton used for US army uniforms.
Chintz – A printed plain weave cotton that is often glazed for furnishings.
Ciré – A waxed satin fabric.
Corduroy – A ribbed cotton velvet used for trousers or cords.
Crash – A coarse linen fabric with a rough texture.
Crêpe – A lightweight fabric with a wrinkled surface of silk, cotton or wool.
Cretonne – A flowery printed plain weave cotton for furnishing fabrics.
Damask – A decorated silk, cotton or linen which is jacquard woven.
Denim – A twill cotton with a white warp and a coloured weft that is strong and hardwearing.
Drill – A coarse cotton or linen used for uniforms.
Flannel – A soft napped wool or worsted fabric.
Flannelette – A soft brushed cotton.
Folkweave – A loosely woven cotton with a woven pattern for furnishings.
Foulard – A soft silk.
Gaberdine – A twill weave wool fabric for outer wear also in cotton and mixtures.
Gauze – A thin transparent cotton, silk or linen.
Gingham – A plain weave check fabric with a woven design.
Hessian – A coarse plain weave open fabric of jute, cotton or linen.
Holland – A coarse brown linen or cotton used for stiffening.
Honeycomb – A pattern of cell-like ridges and hollows made from cotton for furnishings.
Interlock – A smooth knitted ribbed fabric in cotton, wool or a mixture for underwear.
Jacquard – A very decorative weave in silk or cotton.
Jean – A twill cotton used for jeans with the same colour warp and weft.
Jersey – A knitted fabric, single or double made from wool, cotton, silk, or man-made fibres.
Lawn – A fine soft cotton used for underwear, handkerchiefs and linen.
Melton – A heavy woollen fabric with a milled finish and raised surface.
Muslin – A soft, fine, open cloth made from cotton, it is often spotted, striped or corded.
Needlecord – A fine ribbed velvet the width of a needle between the cords of cotton.
Organdie – A stiff, transparent fabric of cotton.
Piqué – Ribbed cotton with a crisp finish.
Poplin – A crosswise ribbed weave in good quality cotton that is often mercerised.
Plaid – A tartan design in a twilled wool.
Print – A printed cotton fabric with a plain weave.
Raschel – A ribbed knitted fabric.
Sateen – A cotton weft satin.

Satin – A smooth shiny fabric with a dull backing made from silk, acetate or polyester.

    Duchesse satin – A rich lustrous satin for dresses.

    Slipper satin – A heavy satin for wedding and evening dresses.

Seersucker – A puckered fabric in striped bands.

Serge – A strong worsted twill fabric of wool.

Shantung – A strong silk fabric rough in texture with a slubbed surface.

Slub – A linen fabric with a bumpy surface caused by thick slubs of yarn.

Taffeta – A ribbed silk, rayon or man-made fibre. Shot effects give two colours.

Tapestry – A woven fabric that looks embroidered, used for upholstery.

Terry – A towelling fabric with a looped surface made from cotton.

Tricot – A knitted fabric with vertical lines on the right side and a crosswise pattern on the back.

Tweed – A rough texture wool with a surface hairiness.

Twill – Any fabric in a twill weave, cotton, wool or man-made fibre. It is strong and resilient.

Velvet – A pile fabric of cotton, silk or synthetic fibres.

Velveteen – A weft pile fabric of cotton.

Velour – A short pile fabric of wool, cotton and synthetic.

Voile – A sheer, transparent cotton, silk or rayon.

Whipcord – A worsted fabric with a cord twill weave.

Pupil participation

Working briefs

1. Making yarn   Individual work (Investigation)

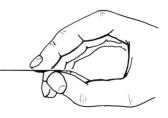

- Take a ball of fibres in your left hand.
- With the thumb and forefinger of your right hand, pull and twist a few fibres.
- Continue to pull and twist them in the same direction until you have a length of yarn.
- Examine your length of yarn for evenness, strength and fineness.
- Try another type of fibre.
- Compare the two lengths of yarn for strength and ease of making.
- Which type of twist did you use?

2. Making a corded yarn   Pair work (Investigation)

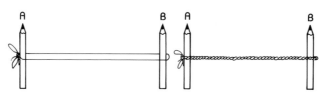
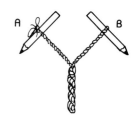

- Working in twos, measure out a metre of 2 ply, 3 ply or 4 ply yarn.
- Fasten each end of the length of yarn to a pencil.
- Stand facing your partner, holding one of the pencils each and pass the yarn over your partner's pencil and back to the first one to tie it.
- Turn each pencil clockwise, holding the yarn tightly stretched.
- Continue to twist the yarns until they are very tightly twisted.
- Bring the pencils together and allow the cord to twist.
- Smooth out any uneven loops that may form, remove the pencils and tie the ends together.

Use the cord-making technique to make a cord for a bathrobe or dressing gown, a belt or tie, a drawstring bag or another article which uses a cord for fastening.

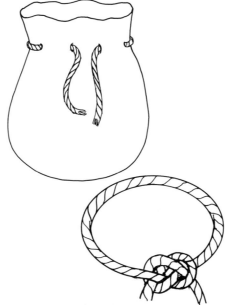

3. Spinning
Class work (Video and guest speaker)

a) Watch the video *Join In and Spin* – produced by Thames Valley, to see the history of spinning, yarn preparation and spinning techniques.
b) Invite a local spinner to come to your school to demonstrate the use of a spinning wheel. Volunteer to write to the person or act as host/hostess during the visit or to thank the person after the demonstration.
c) Try spinning yourself, either with a hand spindle or spinning wheel, alternatively, you could join a course at a study centre such as the one at Quarry Bank Mill, Styal, Cheshire.

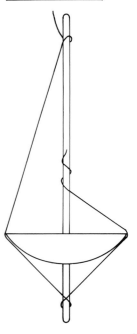

4. Textile technology
Class work (Visit)

Visit a local textile mill, knitwear manufacturing plant or working museum if there are any in your area. Examples are given in the resources guide on page 104. Before you go:

- Find out about the fibre you are going to see.
- Research the fibre's history, processing and manufacture.

Take with you:

- worksheet if available
- clipboard and pencil.

Look out for:

- safety regulations
- new technology
- training schemes.

5. Making a textured yarn   Group work (Investigation)

You will need:

- a length of nylon or polyester filament yarn.
- a Bunsen burner, tripod, gauze mat or pan and stove.
- a glass rod or metal knitting needle.

Method

a) Wrap the filament yarn tightly around the rod.
b) Heat some water in a beaker or container.
c) Place the rod into the container of hot water.
d) Bring to the boil and simmer for 15 minutes.
e) Leave to cool before touching and unwinding the yarn.
f) The yarn should be curled and textured.

Can you create other forms of texture in this way by using square or triangular rods?

6. Weaving   Individual or pair work (Computer design)

Use the *Harris Loom Tutor Program* produced by Emmerich (Berlon) Ltd to create woven patterns in coloured yarns with or without the use of shafts. By using the computer program and working on a *Harris NC Loom*®, it is possible to test out the designs you have created by working a sample.

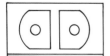

7. Knitting   Class work (Video and community project)

If you are a beginner to knitting then you should watch the video *Basic Hand Knitting* produced by Soft Options. Practise knitting using a variety of thicknesses of yarn and different sizes of needles.

Knitting tension is very important for garment sizing. All patterns refer to it and advise that you knit a tension square before starting to make any knitted garment. Each pupil should work a tension square in double knitting yarn on size 8 (4 mm) needles, casting on 30 stitches and working 40 rows. The tension can be measured as described in the Appendices on page 102.

The resulting squares can be joined together to make a blanket for a local charity or community project.

8. Computer knitwear designing   Individual work (Design)

You will need:

- BBC computer   ● Brother or Knitmaster electronic knitting machine
- Dataknit software from Clwyd Technics (refer to the resources guide on page 104).

Method

- Do your design on the screen.
- Convert your design into stitches.
- Print out the design.
- Investigate reducing and repeating the design.
- Decide on the final design.
- Feed the information to the knitting machine.
- Work the sample design.

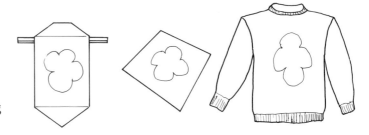

Written work

Fact finding exercise

1. Identify the tools illustrated. These are all used for fabric-making.

2. Suggest a suitable yarn to use with each.

3. Sketch a garment or article made from the resulting fabrics.

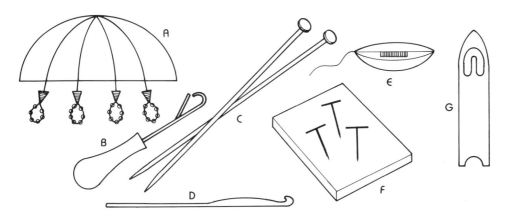

Short answer questions

1. Name one way of measuring the thickness of yarn.

2. What is meant by '4 ply'?

3. Which two letters describe the direction of twist?

4. Name a yarn which has thick untwisted sections along the length.

5. List five ways of making fabric.

6. What is meant by 'fabric with nap'?

Application of knowledge

1. Use the Glossary of fabrics on page 83 to complete the chart with five examples of fabrics traditionally made from the fibres named.

	Cotton	Linen	Wool	Silk
1.				
2.				
3.				
4.				
5.				

2. Refer to the Glossary of fabrics again to choose suitable fabrics for the following items and give reasons for your choices:
   a) Summer shorts
   b) Winter coat
   c) Head wrap
   d) Cushion cover
   e) Table cloth

Structured questions

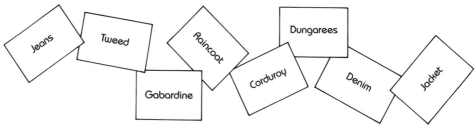

Jeans   Tweed   Raincoat   Dungarees   Gabardine   Corduroy   Denim   Jacket

1. Match the garments to the fabrics using each only once. Make up four more of your own.

2. The symbol illustrated could be found on one of the garments. Explain the symbol and say which garment it belongs to.

3. Raincoats can be waterproof or showerproof. Explain the difference.

4. Corduroy is a fabric with a pile. What care must be taken when laying a paper pattern onto it before cutting it out?

5. Jeans are very popular with teenagers. Give reasons for their popularity.

6. Denim is a fashion fabric at present. Explain how a traditional workwear fabric has changed its image.

Data response

READY SWEATER

Measurements: to fit 81 (87, 92, 97) cm/32 (34, 36, 38) in bust; actual measurements 90 (96, 100, 106) cm/35½ (37¾, 39½, 41¾) in, length 61 cm/24 in, sleeve seam 18.5 cm/7¼ in.

Materials: Phildar Satine No 4, 5 (5, 6, 6) 50g (103m) balls in Blanc (MS) and 4 (5, 5, 6) balls in Drapeau (C); pair each size 3¼ mm/No 10 and 4 mm/no 8 needles. The cost of yarn for the smallest size is £11.61; see Prima directory for stockist details.

Tension: 21 sts and 29 rows to 10 cm over st-st using 4 mm needles.

Abbreviations: alt – alternate; beg – beginning; C – contrast; cm – centimetres; cont – continue; dec – decrease; foll – following; inc – increase; K – knit; MS – main shade; P – purl; patt – pattern; rem – remaining; rep – repeat; RS – right side; st(s) – stitches; st-st – stocking stitch; WS – wrong side.

Note: instructions for the larger sizes are given in round ( ) brackets. Directions in square [ ] brackets are worked the number of times stated. Yarn quantities are approximate as they are based on average requirements.

BACK AND FRONT
(Alike.) Using 3¼ mm needles and MS cast on 86 (92, 98, 104) sts. Work 11 rows in K 1, P 1 rib. **Inc row:** (WS) rib and inc 8 sts evenly across row 94 (100, 106, 112) sts. Change to 4 mm needles and st-st, work 16 rows. Work 28 rows in C, [28 rows in MS, 28 rows in C] twice, then 20 rows in MS. Change to 3¼ mm needles and work 8 rows in K 1, P 1 rib. Cast off in rib.

SLEEVES
Using 3¼ mm needles and MS, cast on 60 sts and work 7 rows in K 1, P 1 rib. **Inc row:** (WS) rib and inc 4 sts evenly across row. 64 sts. Change to 4 mm needles and st-st, inc 1 st at each end of next and every foll 3rd row, until there are 86 sts. *At the same time*, work 20 rows in MS then 20 rows in C. Cast off loosely.

TO MAKE UP
Overlap top rib edges at shoulders and sew in position. Matching centre of cast off edge of sleeve to centre of overlapped shoulder ribs, sew on sleeves. Join side and sleeve seams, matching stripes.

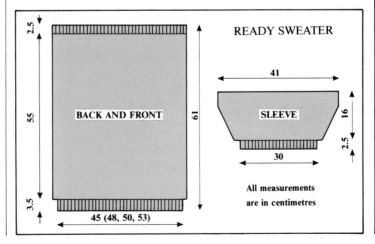

READY SWEATER

BACK AND FRONT

SLEEVE

All measurements are in centimetres

1. How many pieces are needed to make the sweater?

2. How many sizes are given in the instructions?

3. Give details of the smallest sweater, its size, actual measurements and sleeve length.

4. How much yarn will be needed to knit the largest size?

5. Give two examples of contrasting colour schemes that it could be knitted in.

6. How much does the sweater cost to knit? Do you consider this good value or not? Give reasons for your answer.

7. Explain the meaning of the term 'tension' when knitting. How can tension be tested before knitting?

8. The stripes of the sweater are horizontal. Discuss the effect of this type of stripe on a plump figure.

Free response

Plan a talk on non-woven fabrics and their uses under the following headings:
- How non-woven fabrics are made.
- What they are used for.
- The good and bad points of non-woven fabrics.

Self-assessment ————————————

Photocopy and complete the self-assessment chart on page 161, inserting the following list of topics under 'The work I have done includes':

1. Spinning
2. Yarn thickness
3. Textured and novelty yarns
4. Weaving
5. Knitting
6. Non-woven fabrics
7. Fabric names.

Photocopy and complete the self-marking plan on page 162 for the eight working briefs in this unit.

Fabric finishes

Core information

Grey fabric

When a fabric comes straight from the loom or knitting machine it is unsuitable for sale. It is often unattractive, unfinished and a greige (grey/beige) colour. It is called **grey fabric**. It has to go through three processes before it can be sold:

- cleaning
- colouring
- finishing.

Cleaning

There are four main cleaning processes:

- Scouring – a thorough cleaning to remove grease, dirt and stains.
- Bleaching – whitening the fabric with bleach to obtain an even colour.
- Desizing – softening the fabric by washing away starches added for weaving.
- Singeing – burning off the surface hairiness.

Colouring

This is done in two ways:

- dyeing
- printing.

The picture shows the huge dyeing machine that is used commercially to dye large amounts of fabric.

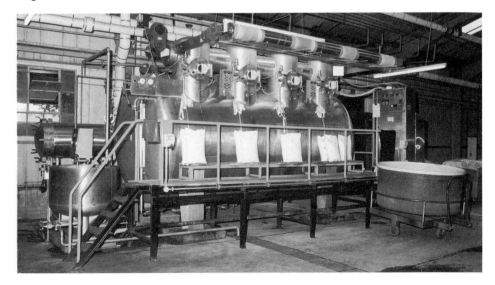

Animal dyes	Vegetable dyes	Mineral dyes
Red – cochineal (Mexican insect) Purple–murex (sea snail) Scarlet–kermes (insect)	Blue–indigo Red–madder Blue–woad Yellow–saffron Black–logwood Red–safflower	Iron buff Chrome yellow Chrome orange Manganese bronze Prussian blue Mineral khaki

Modern dyeing uses a variety of dyes, matching the type of dye to the type of fibre.

Dye type	Description	Fibre
Vat	Strong, fast, dyed in a vat.	Cellulose, protein
Direct	No mordant needed, cheap, moderate fastness.	Cellulose
Reactive	Reacts chemically with cellulose.	Cellulose
Acid	Applied by an acid bath.	Protein, polyamide
Basic	Non-fast, bright colours.	Protein, acrylic
Disperse	Fast, insoluble, chemical reaction dye.	Synthetics

Stages of dyeing

Dyeing can be carried out at different stages in the production process:

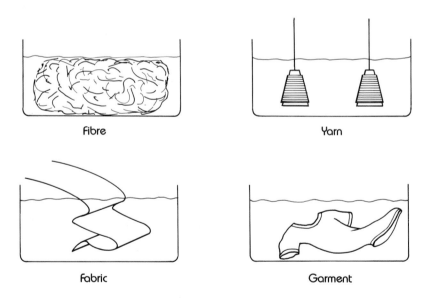

Fibre

Yarn

Fabric

Garment

- At the fibre stage the dye penetrates well. Colours can be blended which is useful in heather mixtures.
- At the yarn stage the coloured yarns can be twisted together. Dyed yarns can be woven into designs.
- At the fabric stage the colour can be decided later. There are large amounts to handle.
- The advantage of dyeing at the garment stage is that up-to-date colours are possible, however the dye is not as thorough.

Printing

Printing involves applying colour to the surface of the fabric. It can be carried out in several ways:

- Block printing which is a hand craft, is slow and requires great skill.
- Roller printing which needs expensive engraved copper rollers.
- Screen printing by hand is slow and is used for expensive silk fabrics.
- Rotary screen printing which is quicker and widely used.
- Transfer printing which is quicker, cheaper, up-to-date and suitable for difficult fabrics.
- Block, roller and screen printing all use liquid dye to print the design onto the cloth.
- Transfer printing uses no water so it works well on non-absorbent fibres.
- Transfer printing does not need extra setting processes to make it fast.

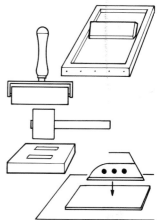

Block printing

Roller printing

Screen printing

Fabric finishes

Finishes can:

- improve the appearance of a fabric • improve fabric wear • develop new and beneficial properties.

The picture shows a roller raising machine finishing knitted jersey fabric with a brushed backing. This is a mechanical finishing process and other mechanical processes include:

- Beetling – a polishing and flattening process.
- Calendering – a smoothing, shining and flattening process.
- Milling – a thickening and matting process.
- Stentering – a stretching and straightening process.
- Compacting – a shrinking process.

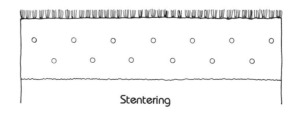

Stentering

The results of stentering can be seen when examining the selvedges of fabric and noting the holes along the length of the fabric on each side. These are stentering holes from the stenter machine.

Fabric finishes can also be chemical in origin. Chemicals are applied to the surface of fabrics to make them resistant to:

- fire - water - stains - creasing - insect attack - micro-organism attack - static - shrinking.

Chemicals can also improve fabric properties by:

- strengthening - stiffening - permanently creasing.

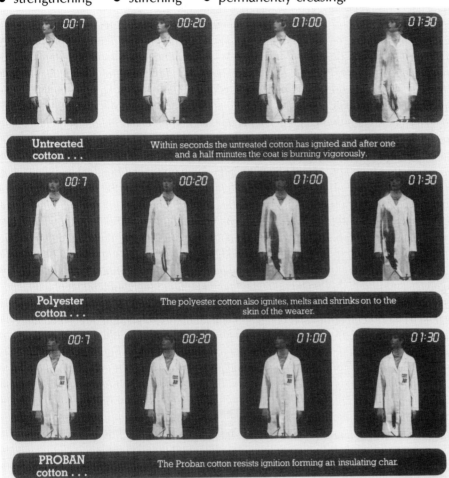

Untreated cotton . . . Within seconds the untreated cotton has ignited and after one and a half minutes the coat is burning vigorously.

Polyester cotton . . . The polyester cotton also ignites, melts and shrinks on to the skin of the wearer.

PROBAN cotton . . . The Proban cotton resists ignition forming an insulating char.

The chart lists the finishes, trade names and fibres which benefit from being treated.

Finish	Trade names	Fibres
Flameproof	Proban®, Pyrovatex®, Zirpro®	Cotton, wool
Water-repellant	Dri-sil®, Velan®	Cotton
Stain-resistant	Zepel®, Scotchguard®	Most types
Crease-resistant	Tebilised®, Permalose®, Easycare®	Cellulose
Mothproof	Mitin®, Eulan®, Dielmoth®	Wool
Bacteria-proof	Actifresh®, Durafresh®, Sanitised®	Cellulose
Antistatic	AntiStat®, Zerostat®	Synthetics
Shrink-resist	Sanforised®, Rigmel®, Superwash®	Cotton, wool
Strengthening	Mercerisation®	Cotton
Stiffening	Trubenised®	Cotton
Permanent press	Koratron®, Fixaform®, Lintrak®	Synthetics, wool

Pupil participation

Working briefs

1. Fabric colouration   Individual work (Investigation)

a) Examine a selection of dyed and printed fabrics carefully, looking at both sides of the fabric. Fray the threads on one side and look at the colouring.

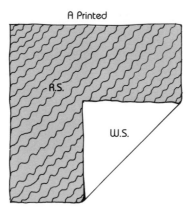

A Printed

R.S.

W.S.

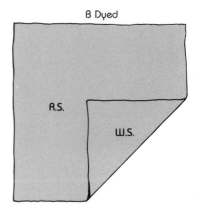

B Dyed

R.S.

W.S.

Answer the following questions about each fabric:

- How was the fabric constructed?
- Is the fabric dyed or printed?
- At what stage was the dye applied?
- Is the dye fast?

b) In order to find out about the fastness of the dye, you will need:

- an iron   • a clean white pressing cloth.

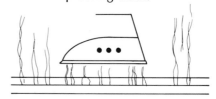

Dampen the pressing cloth and press each fabric with it, looking for signs of colour transferring to the cloth after each pressing. If the dye is fast, no colour should be evident.

2. Testing colour fastness to light
Group work (Investigation)

This test takes several weeks before a result is obvious.

- Cut two squares of fabric from five different samples of brightly coloured cloth.
- Place one square of each sample into an envelope and seal it.
- Fasten the other five pieces to a strip of paper as shown.

- Tape the strip to a south-facing window with the fabrics facing the sun and leave for at least three weeks.
- Remove the strip and compare the individual pieces with those in the envelope.

3. Dyeing and printing
Group work (Video)

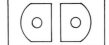

Watch one of these videos which shows the dyeing and printing of fabric:
- *English Silk* produced by the Film Corporation of Ireland
- *A Riot of Colour* produced by BBC Enterprises, Textile Studies, Programme 4.

After watching the video, try printing or silk painting for yourself.

4. Colour
Group work (Visit)

Try to arrange a visit to the Colour Museum, Perkin House, Bradford.
Look out for:
- Displays telling the story of dyes, dyeing and textile printing
- Audio visual programmes about fashion and textiles
- Experiments mixing light and colour
- Information on matching colours.

5. Water-resistant fabric finishes
Group work (Investigation)

Test a selection of fabrics for their resistance to water. The selection should include:
- different fabric constructions
- loosely and closely set threads
- water-repellant finishes
- different fibres.

The diagram shows the different effects of a drop of water on the surfaces of different fabrics. The left-hand side shows the least water-repellant and the right-hand side shows the most repellant.

Using a dropper, put one drop of water onto the surface of each fabric and leave it for two minutes before shaking off any which has not been absorbed. Compare the area of wetness on each fabric and draw conclusions as to the water repellancy of each fabric. Refer to the Appendices on page 103.

6. The labelling of different fabric finishes
Individual work (Investigation and discussion)

Look through your clothes at home for a label which has a finishing process named on it. Look for labels such as: Superwash, Waterproof, Machine washable, Cling resist, *Scotchguard®*, *Koratron®*, *Sanforised®*, etc.

Bring one garment into school for a discussion on the advantages of fabric finishes for your clothes.
Has your garment been improved by the application of a finish?

7. Functional clothing
Individual work (Design)

A waterproof jacket has to be functional but a designer could find ways of making it look more individual and attractive. Sketch ideas for a designer kaghoul based on the shape suggested. Add trousers and a sweater to the outfit and suggest individual designs for these as well.

Written work

Application of knowledge

The labels shown have been lost from their garments. The garments have been listed on the left. Match the label to the garment and write briefly about each finish.

1. Nylon slip
2. Child's pyjamas
3. Trousers
4. Anorak
5. Woollen jumper.

PROBAN®
B.S. 3120
DURABLE FLAME-RETARDANT FINISH
HOT WASH WITH DETERGENT
DO NOT BOIL
NO SOAP OR SOAP POWDERS
NO HYPOCHLORITE BLEACH
DRY CLEANABLE

SUPER 40 Denier
CLING RESIST
NYLON GARMENT

Structured questions

The picture shows a cotton fibre under the microscope after it has been mercerised.

1. What chemical is used in the mercerisation process?

2. Why is the process so named?

3. Draw the cotton fibre before mercerisation.

4. In what ways has cotton been improved by the process?

5. List four other finishes applied to cotton and describe one in detail.

6. Describe the processing of cotton from boll to fabric.

7. Cotton is the world's most popular fabric. Explain why it is so good for clothing.

Short answer questions

Explain the need for the following:

1. A *Sanforised*® label on your new jeans.

2. *Trubenised*® shirt collars.

3. *Actifresh*® shower curtains.

4. A *Dielmoth*® finish on a wool carpet.

5. Bleaching fabric before dyeing it.

Data response

**MVT PROOFING RATED 6.2 LITRES
MOISTURE VAPOUR TRANSMISSION
"REDUCES CONDENSATION" ALL
WELDED TAPED SEAMS**

This garment is unique in that Peter Storm has achieved, in his own plant, a 100% waterproof proofing called MVT that transmits 6.2 litres of water vapour through 1 square metre of fabric in 24 hours.
Features:
*Guaranteed 100% wind and waterproof.
*Limits condensation, water cannot get in, but condensation can get out.
*Hand or machine washable at 40°C.
We hereby guarantee for one year to rectify or replace this garment if it fails to meet the high standard of its manufacture. Please retain your Purchase Receipt.
The above does not affect your Statutory Rights.
Did you know:
Peter Storm manufactures 5 different ranges of foul weather gear. Also proofed wool sweaters, caps, chlorofibre thermal wear, socks and buoyancy aids.

The swing ticket illustrated was attached to a waterproof jacket.

1. Explain the letters MVT and the numbers 6.2 on the label.

2. What advantage are 'welded taped seams'?

3. What does the guarantee promise?

4. What claims are made about the fabric of the jacket?

5. List the range of Peter Storm products.

6. Explain the term 'Statutory Rights'.

Free response

Wool was a problem fibre in the past, however modern finishing processes have improved it as a clothing fibre.

Write about the changes which have taken place in wool as a clothing fibre such as machine washing, mothproofing and permanent pleating. Suggest how wool can also be used as a household fabric.

Self-assessment

Photocopy and complete the self-assessment chart on page 161, inserting the following list of topics under 'The work I have done includes':

1. Cleaning grey fabric
2. Commercial dyeing
3. Commercial printing
4. Fabric finishes
5. Trade names.

Photocopy and complete the self-marking plan on page 162 for the seven working briefs in this unit.

Appendices – Study Area 2

Unit 1

How to make your own slides for microscopic identification

Longitudinal identification

Separate the fibres and place one fibre onto a glass slide. Add a drop of liquid (liquid paraffin or water) and cover with a cover glass or a second slide.

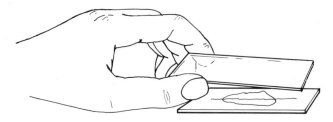

Cross-sectional identification

Using a section plate or a piece of metal with a small hole in the centre, pull a loop of yarn through the hole. The fit must be very tight indeed if it is to stay in place. Cut the yarn above and below the plate with a razor blade. A section should stay in the centre if the yarn is tight enough.

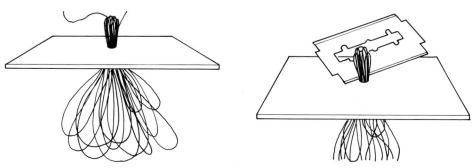

Fibre identification using chemicals

A fibre can be identified by detecting the presence of a substance within it. Two or more tests are needed for a positive identification.

Take great care when using chemicals and follow the safety rules.

Test	Fibres	Chemical	Method
Protein	Wool Silk	50% nitric acid solution Ammonium hydroxide solution	1. Put a few fibres in a test tube and add a few drops of 50% nitric acid solution. 2. Heat very gently in a Bunsen flame. 3. Look for a yellow colour. 4. Cool the test tube. 5. Add a few drops of ammonium hydroxide. 6. An **orange** colour shows that protein is present.
Cellulose	Cotton Linen Viscose	60% sulphuric acid solution Iodine solution	1. Put a few fibres in a watch glass. 2. Add a little 60% sulphuric acid solution and leave a few minutes. 3. Transfer the fibres with tweezers to a container with iodine solution in it. 4. If a **blue/black** colour appears after a few minutes, cellulose is present.
Acetone	Acetate	Acetone	1. Place a few fibres in a watch glass. 2. Add pure acetone and stir. 3. Leave for at least 10 minutes. 4. If the fibres dissolve then they are acetate.
Concentrated HCl	Silk Viscose Acetate Polyamide	Concentrated hydrochloric acid	1. Place a few fibres in a watch glass, test tube or container. 2. Add a few drops of concentrated hydrochloric acid. 3. Leave for a few minutes. 4. Look for disintegration of the fibres.
Nitrogen	Polyamide Acrylic	Soda lime	1. Put a few fibres into a test tube and add a few granules of soda lime. 2. Heat strongly in a Bunsen flame to drive off a gas. 3. Test the gas with a moist strip of red litmus-paper placed in the mouth of the tube. 4. A **blue** colour denotes that nitrogen is present.
Sulphur	Wool	10% sodium hydroxide solution Lead acetate solution	1. Add a few fibres to a little sodium hydroxide solution in a beaker. 2. Leave for 30 minutes. 3. Heat the container gently to boiling point. 4. Cool and test for sulphur with a few drops of lead acetate solution. 5. Look for a **black/brown** colour.

Unit 2

Knitting tension

Every knitting pattern advises you to knit a tension square using the yarn that they recommend and the size of needles that they recommend. Their calculations for sizing are based on these and it is necessary to check that your knitting will come out the same size.

How to check tension

1. Cast on the number of stitches that they recommend using the size of needles recommended.

2. Work the number of rows that they suggest using stocking stitch (knit a row, purl a row)

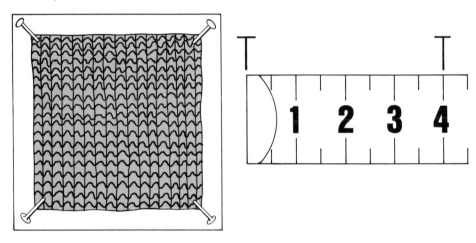

3. Cast off the stitches and lay the knitted piece flat on a table.

4. Measure a square the size suggested in the instructions and count the stitches across and downwards.

5. If you have more stitches and rows than the pattern suggests then your tension is tight and you need a larger needle.

6. If you have less stitches and rows then your tension is slack and you need a smaller needle.

Double knitting tension exercise

1. Having worked on size 8 (4 mm) needles with 30 stitches for 40 rows, measure the tension of your knitting as described over 5 cm.

2. Record your tension on a class chart.

Name	Stitches	Rows

3. If an average tension is 14 stitches across and 16 rows down, is your tension tight or slack? Do you need larger or smaller needles?

Unit 3

Water-resistant fabric finishes

Carry out the experiment suggested and after the time allowed compare the area of wetness and complete the chart below. Examples are given:

Fabric	Fibre	Construction	Observation	Conclusion
1.	PVC	Laminated	No penetration	Waterproof
2.	Cotton	Woven	Large wet area	Absorbent
3.	Polycotton	Woven	Slight dampness	Proofed fabric

Resources guide

Useful addresses

The Knitting Craft Group, PO Box 6, Thirsk, North Yorkshire YO7 1TA
British Wool Marketing Board, Oak Mills, Station Road, Clayton, Bradford, West Yorkshire
British Man-made Fibres Federation, 24 Buckingham Gate, London SW1E 6LB
Lever Bros. Ltd, 3 St James Road, Kingston-upon-Thames, Surrey KT1 2BA
J & P Coats Ltd, Thread Advisory Service, 12 Seedhill Road, Paisley, Scotland PA1 1JT
English Sewing Ltd, 56 Oxford Street, Manchester M60 1HJ
International Wool Secretariat, Wool House, 6 Carlton Gardens, London
International Linen, 31 Great Queen Street, London WC2B 5AA

Books

Books	Publisher
Handbook of Textiles, A. Collier	Wheaton
Technology of Textile Properties, M. Taylor	Forbes
From Fibres to Fabrics, E. Gale	Allman
Textiles, E. Miller	Batsford
Fibres and Fabrics of Today, H. Thompson	Heinemann
Shire Albums – *Cotton Industry*	
– *Flax and Linen*	
– *Looms and Weaving*	
– *Spinning and Spinning Wheels*	
– *Textile Printing*	
– *Woollen Industry*	
– *Pillow Lace and Bobbins*	
– *Crochet*	
Mary Thomas' Knitting Book	Hodder and Stoughton
The Craft of Hand Spinning, E. Chadwick	Batsford
Macramé, M. Walker Phillips	Pan Craft Books
Introducing Macramé, E. Short	Batsford
Making Needlecraft Landscapes, M. Caroll	David and Charles

Designing with String, M. Sneyd   Batsford
Fabric Pictures, E. Alexander   Mills and Boon
Screen Printing, S. Hollebone
The Creative Use of Yarn, J. Messant
Fibres and Fabrics, Nuffield Home   Hutchinson
Economics

Teaching kits

	Source
The Wool Connection	CBWT 60 Toller Lane, Bradford BD8 9BZ
Fibres and Fabrics Packs (Nuffield):	Nottingham Educational Supplies
Textile Testing Programme	Ludlow Hill Road,
Natural Fibre Resource Pack	West Bridgeford,
Spinning and Dyeing Programme	Nottingham
Natural Dyeing Programme	
Weaving Programme	

Videos

	Source
Textile Studies	BBC Enterprises Ltd, 80 Wood Lane, London W12 0TT
Join In and Spin	Thames Valley Productions, Nottingham Educational Supplies
The Story of Linen Fil d'Or	International Linen Promotions Ltd, 31 Great Queen St, London
English Silk	Film Corporation of Ireland, Bridgesglen Road, Shankhill, Dublin, Ireland
All In A Day (crochet and lace)	Coats Viyella, Nottingham Educational Supplies
Soft Options (hand knitting)	Knitting Craft Group, PO Box 6, Thirsk, North Yorkshire

Software

Harris Loom Weave Program: T1 and T2	Emmerich (Berlon) Ltd, Wotton Road, Ashford, Kent
Dataknit	Clwyd Technics, Antelope Industrial Estate, Rhydymwyn, Nr. Mold, Clwyd

Places to visit

Cambrian Factory, Llanwrytyd Wells, Powys LD5 4SD
Bradford Industrial Museum, Moorside Road, Bradford BD2 3HP
British Wool Centre, Marketing Board, Oak Mills, Station Road, Clayton, Bradford BD4 6JD
Macclesfield Silk Museum, Paradise Mill, Park Lane, Macclesfield SK11 6TL
Quarry Bank Mill, Styal, Cheshire SK9 4LA
Lullingstone Silk Farm, Compton House, Sherborne, Dorset DT9 4QW
David Evans and Co Ltd, Silk printers and dyers, Bourne Road, Crayford, Kent DA1 4BP

UNIT ONE

Household textiles

Study Area 3

Core information

Textiles in the home

Textiles play an important part in the home. They give us warmth, privacy, protection, comfort and pleasant surroundings. When choosing textiles for the home we should consider:

- aesthetics
- efficiency
- safety
- hygiene
- economy.

Duvets

- Duvets are increasingly replacing traditional bedding; one quilt is used with fitted sheets, a frilled valance and pillows.
- Duvets are bought according to their **tog** rating.

Summer			Autumn/Spring		Winter		
4.5 tog	6 tog	7.5 tog	9 tog	10.5 tog	12 tog	13.5 tog	15 tog

- A tog is a unit of thermal resistance.
- The higher the tog the warmer the quilt.
- Fillings can be shaken down in the summer months.
- All-year-round duvets are two quilts, one removable in the summer.
- Electric duvets with thermostatically controlled heat can be bought.

Duvet fillings

Duvets can be filled with:

- Down, goose down is the best quality.
- Feathers used alone or with down.
- Polyester, terylene P3, or special hollow fibre filling.

Advantages of duvets

There are several advantages of using duvets:

- Bed-making is quick and easy.
- Duvets are light in weight but warm.

A duvet gives you extra time in bed

- They are less restricting to movement in sleep.
- They can be attractive and part of the furnishing scheme.
- They are economical as less bedding is needed.

Carpets

The earliest carpets were Eastern in origin coming from Persia, Turkey, India and China. They were skilfully made using traditional designs in wool and silk. Modern carpets can be made by:

- weaving
- tufting
- bonding
- needle punching.

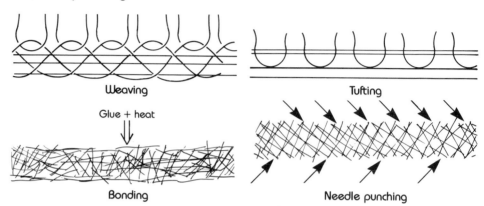

Weaving

Tufting

Glue + heat

Bonding

Needle punching

The chart shows the fibres used for carpets, their trade names, quality and related costs.

Fibre	Wool	Nylon	Acrylic	Polypropylene
Trade name		Antron® Bri-Nylon® Timbrelle® Enkalon®	Courtelle® Dralon® Acrilan® Taklan®	Merkalon®
Quality	Excellent	Very good	Good	Very good
Cost	High	Moderate	High	Low

Quality is determined by

- construction method   ● fibre   ● weight   ● thickness   ● height of pile   ● density of pile.

Manufacturers who are members of the British Carpet Manufacturers Assocation have a carpet labelling scheme, the British Carpet Performance Rating Label (British Carpet Mark).

Grade	Wear	Use
A	Extra heavy wear	Commercial
B	Very heavy wear	Stairs
C	Heavy wear	Living rooms, halls, kitchens
D	General wear	Dining rooms, studies
E	Medium wear	Bedrooms
F	Light wear	Spare bedrooms

A European labelling scheme with only four grades will be introduced in 1992.

Curtains

There are various types of curtains:

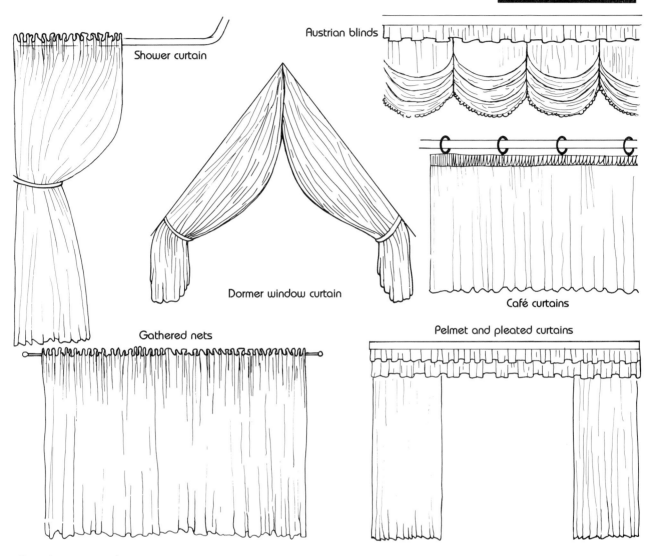

Shower curtain

Austrian blinds

Dormer window curtain

Café curtains

Gathered nets

Pelmet and pleated curtains

Curtains are used to:

- provide privacy
- give warmth to a room
- add to the furnishing of a room
- protect a room from sunlight.

They are made from many types of fabric including cotton, polyester, acrylic, glassfibre, silk, viscose, polyamide and mixture fabrics. Flameproof curtains can be made from modacrylic or treated cottons.

When choosing fabric for curtains consider:

- weight of the fabric for hanging
- closeness of the weave as a barrier against cold draughts
- resistance to fading and rotting with sunlight
- washability.

Lined curtains can help with insulation against cold and heat. Curtain linings help the wear of the curtains, protect the fabric from fading and improve the hanging quality of the curtains.

Blinds are replacing curtains in many rooms such as bathrooms, kitchens, playrooms and studies.

Upholstery

This term includes the covering fabric and the padding in furniture. The graph shows the most popular fabrics used for covering furniture.

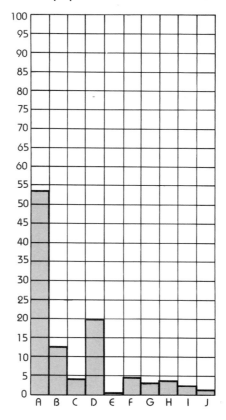

Key

A Plain pile fabric
B Sculptured pile
C Plain flat weave
D Print
E Chintz
F Jacquard
G Tapestry
H Leather
I Vinyl
J Others

The fibres used for these fabrics include acrylic, cotton, wool, polyester and polyamide.

Since 1989 highly flammable foam fillings have been banned from use in furniture. The Furniture and Furnishings (Fire and Safety) Regulations 1988 stated that from March 1989:

- All furniture must pass the cigarette test.
- All furniture must carry permanent labels.
- All non-foam fillings must pass tests.
- All loose filling material must pass tests.

All new furniture must contain foam which is combustion modified high resilient foam (CMHR).

At present second-hand furniture does not have to comply with the new regulations but from 1993 it will have to follow the same rules as new furniture. In the meantime a yellow warning label may be displayed.

Loose covers

Furniture can be bought with removeable loose covers when it is new. Alternatively, covers can be made for old furniture in order to improve its appearance. Loose covers can:

- prolong the life of furniture
- protect the fabric
- be washed when necessary
- fit existing furniture into a new colour scheme
- disguise wear and tear.

Bedding

Type	Fabric	Filling	Style
Sheets	Cotton Linen Polycotton		Flat Fitted single Double King-sized
Pillow cases	Cotton Linen Polycotton	Down Feather Latex Polyester Foam	Plain Frilled
Blankets	Wool Acrylic		Traditional Cellular Electric
Bedspreads	Cotton Candlewick Lace Nylon		Throw-over Fitted Patchwork Quilted
Eiderdowns	Downproofing	Down/feather Polyester	Plain Frilled

Household items

Type	Fabric	Style
Towels	Cotton Linen union	Bath, hand, guest, beach, tea-towel, roller
Table Linen	Linen Cotton Polycotton	Table-cloth, table mats, napkins
Lampshades	Silk Polyester Acetate	Plain, pleated, swathed, panelled
Cushions	Velvet Furnishing Linen Cottons	Plain, frilled, piped, embroidered, tapestry, quilted, appliqué, patchwork, smocked, tie-dyed, batik

Insulation

Glassfibre can be used to insulate a loft to reduce heat loss through the roof of a house. Hot water tanks can be lagged with padded jackets and pipes can be protected by lagging to prevent freezing in the winter. Draughts can be reduced by putting curtains over doors, using reflective backed blinds and draught excluders.

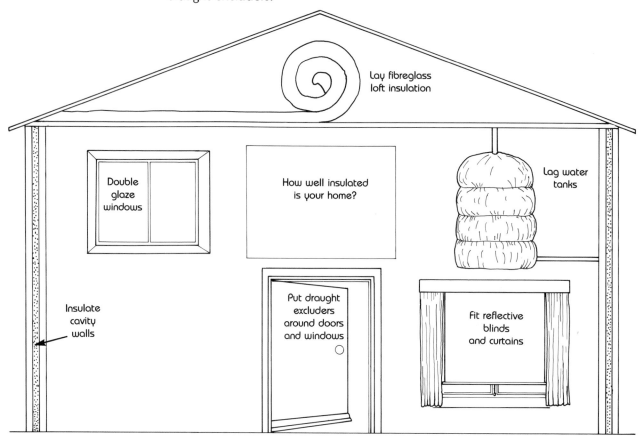

Textile care in the home

Equipment

Clothes and household textiles pick up dirt and stains in everyday use. They will need cleaning in order to:

- be hygienic and healthy to wear
- maintain a good appearance
- prolong the wear of the fabric.

In the UK 85% of households own a washing machine and as the chart shows, 75% of these are automatic machines, 20% are twin tubs and 5% are old single tub machines.

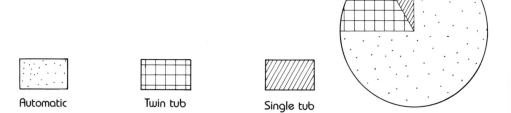

Automatic   Twin tub   Single tub

There are three types of washing action depending on the type of machine:

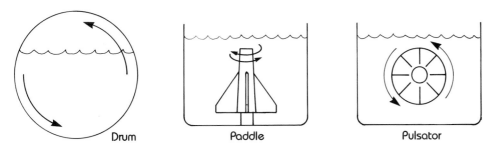

Drum   Paddle   Pulsator

These three types of washing action provide agitation which is necessary for washing efficiency. A washing machine can normally provide more agitation than hand washing and so is more efficient.

The choice of washing machine depends upon:

• space available   • money available   • time for washing   • family size.

Detergents

Water is a detergent, but on its own it is not very good. It has a high surface tension and will remain in drops on the fabric surface. If soap or soapless detergent is added to it, the water will penetrate the fabric. A good detergent should:

• wet the fabric   • loosen the stains   • remove the stains   • hold it in the water so that it can be washed away.

The diagrams illustrate the action of a detergent on a stain.

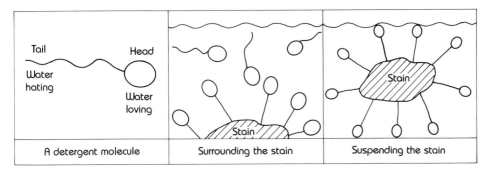

Tail   Head
Water hating   Water loving

A detergent molecule   Surrounding the stain   Suspending the stain

Types of detergent

Here are a few of the detergent products available in a supermarket. There are a wide range of powders and liquids available for washing by hand and machine. Some are soap detergents, others are non-soap detergents (NSD).

A packet of detergent contains:

- Cleaning chemicals
- Water softeners
- Bleach
- Enzymes
- Foaming chemicals
- Colour brighteners
- Dyes and perfumes
- Metal protecting chemicals
- Chemicals to keep powder dry.

Changes in home washing

In recent years there have been a number of changes in the traditional washing patterns in the home:

- More washing is done in the home. (93% of all clothes washing).
- More drying is done by machine.
- Clothes are washed more often.
- Washing is done at any time of the day and week.
- Liquid detergents are increasing in use.
- Cooler water temperatures are being used for washing.
- Improved detergents can wash well at lower temperatures.

The washing process

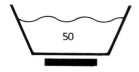

A packet of detergent also has instructions on it giving the correct washing programme for the fabric being washed. These are based on the wash tub symbol which shows three things:
- Water temperature   • amount of agitation   • method of removing water.

The temperature is quickly seen from the numbers in the tub but the agitation and the water removal are shown by the bar symbol beneath the tub.

No Bar	Normal (maximum) machine action	Normal spinning
	Reduced (medium) machine action	Short spin
	Much reduced (minimum) machine action	Normal spinning

Code	Machine	Hand	Sample of application
95	Very hot – to boil Maximum wash / Spin or wring	Hand or boil	White cotton and linen articles without special finishes
60	Hot maximum wash / Spin or wring	Hand hot	Cotton linen or viscose articles without special finishes where colours are fast at 60°C
50	Hand hot medium wash / Cold rinse, short spin or drip dry	Hand hot	Nylon, polyester/cotton mixtures, polyester, cotton and viscose articles with special finishes; cotton/ acrylic mixtures
40	Warm maximum wash / Spin or wring	Warm	Cotton, linen or viscose articles, where colours are fast at 40°C but not at 60°C
40	Warm medium wash / Spin or wring	Warm	Acrylics, acetate and triacetate including mixtures with wool; polyester/wool blends
40	Warm minimum wash / Spin do not hand wring	Warm – do not rub	Wool, wool mixed with other fibres; silks
	Handwash (do not machine wash)		Delicate fabrics
	Do not wash		

Care labelling

The wash tub symbol is one of the international textile care labelling symbols.

	Wash tub	The washing process (hand or machine)
	Triangle	Chlorine bleaching
	Circle in square	Tumble drying
	Iron	Ironing
	Circle	Dry cleaning

The use of symbols makes the instructions easily understood internationally. The code is controlled in the UK by the HLCC (Home Laundering Consultative Council) which is a member of GINETEX, the international textile care labelling association which developed the ITCLC (International Textile Care Labelling Code).

All five symbols are used on care labels which are sewn into all made-up garments. An explanation of the various symbols found on labels follows:

Bleaching

The letters CL indicate that the article may be bleached with chlorine bleach.

Do not bleach, e.g. wool, silk.

Tumble drying

Most textile items can be safely tumble dried and so other instructions are only given if tumble drying is not suitable.

Do not tumble dry.
Imported goods may show these symbols.

 Dry flat   Line dry   Drip dry

Ironing

There are four variations of the iron symbol and the dots show the maximum sole plate temperature.

Hot (200°C) Cotton, linen, viscose or modal.

Warm (150°C) Polyester mixtures, wool.

Cool (110°C) Acrylic, nylon, acetate, triacetate, polyester

Do not iron

Dry-cleaning

The circle symbol shows that the article can be dry-cleaned but the letters A, P or F, inside the circle are additional information for the dry-cleaner or for those using dry-cleaning machines.

A bar placed underneath the circle indicates a sensitivity to dry-cleaning.

Normal goods dry-cleanable in all solvents.

Normal goods dry-cleanable in perchloroethylene, solvent 113, white spirit and solvent 11.

Normal goods dry-cleanable in solvent 113 and white spirit.

Do not dry-clean.

Stain removal

There are three types of staining:

- surface dirt, e.g. dust, mud, smoke
- absorbed dirt and stains, e.g. tea, coffee, food
- compound stains, e.g. paint, oil, grease.

The first two types can be removed by washing action and normal detergents or enzyme detergents. The third type of stain is more difficult to remove and washing could make things worse as hot water sets stains. Certain stains will need a **solvent** to remove them, this is a substance which combines with the stain to make a solution which can then be removed.

Safety precautions

When using solvents take great care:

- Use in a well ventilated room.
- Keep away from flames.
- Wash your hands after using.
- Keep out of the way of young children.
- See that they are clearly labelled.
- Lock away poisonous solvents.

Harmful

Flammable

Toxic

Rules for stain removal

1. Remove the stain as soon as possible.
2. Follow the safety precautions for using solvents.
3. Check that the solvent will not damage the fabric.
4. Identify the nature of the stain.
5. Use the correct solvent.
6. Remove any residue from the surface.
7. Push the stain out from the back.

Stain	Solvent	Stain	Solvent
Adhesive	Acetone (Nail varnish remover)	Iron mould	Salts of lemon
		Lipstick	Grease solvent
Biro	Methylated spirit	Nail varnish	Acetone
Blood	Cold salt water	Paint	White spirit, paraffin or petrol
Chewing gum	Special solvent or freeze		
Chocolate	Grease solvent	Perspiration	Vinegar or ammonia
Curry	Glycerine	Singe	Borax or peroxide
Egg	Enzyme detergent	Shoe polish	Grease solvent
Fruit	Glycerine	Tar	*Thawpit*® or *Dabitoff*®
Grass	Methylated spirit	Urine	*Napisan*®
Grease	Grease solvent	Wax	Grease solvent
Ink	Methylated spirit	Wine	Borax

Fibre content labelling

One way of checking the fibre before treating stains with solvent is to look at the label on the garment. By law (Indication of Fibre Contents Regulations 1973) the fibre content must be listed and every different fibre must be named.

This can be seen on the label illustrated. Notice the care instructions on the same label. The label was found on a pair of stretch jeans.

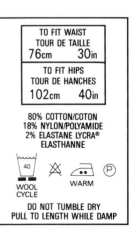

TO FIT WAIST
TOUR DE TAILLE
76cm   30in

TO FIT HIPS
TOUR DE HANCHES
102cm   40in

80% COTTON/COTON
18% NYLON/POLYAMIDE
2% ELASTANE LYCRA®
ELASTHANNE

WOOL CYCLE   WARM

DO NOT TUMBLE DRY
PULL TO LENGTH WHILE DAMP

Pupil participation

Working briefs

1. Choosing fabric
Group work (Investigation)

Curtain fabric should:

- hang well
- keep out draughts
- resist fading from sunlight
- be non-flammable in public places.

Plan four investigations to compare a selection of furnishing fabrics for use as curtain fabrics. Carry out experiments for:

- drape
- closeness of weave
- fading
- flammability.

Record the results and draw conclusions as to the suitability of each fabric tested for curtains. Present the results in chart form. Refer to the Appendices on page 154.

2. Safety in the home
Group work (Guest speaker and poster)

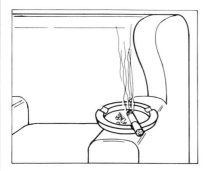  

Invite a speaker from the Fire Service to come and talk to your group about the dangers of fire in the home. Afterwards design a poster to draw attention to the fire risks in a house.

3. Ideal home
Class work (Visit and discussion)

Visit an Ideal Homes Exhibition or something similar in order to see the latest design in homes, furnishings and household textiles.

Take note of:

- new technology
- new fabrics
- creative use of textiles.

On returning to school, everyone in the group should consider the important aspects of the exhibition. Go round the group to get everyone's opinion.

4. Laundry equipment　　Individual work (Investigation)

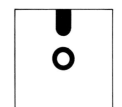

Visit the local electricity showroom or an electrical retailer to obtain information about different makes of washing machines, tumble driers and irons. List names, prices, features, sizes and colours. Make a chart of the results or use the computer program *Soap* produced by Lever Bros.

From the results:
a) Make a list of laundry equipment needed by a young couple setting up home.
b) Cost the items chosen.
c) Give reasons for your choice.

5. Detergent Products　　Individual work (Investigation)

Visit your local supermarket or shop and look at the different types of detergent available on the shelves. Make a chart like the one given and fill in the information.

Product name	Type e.g. automatic	Biological	Liquid or powder	Special features	Weight	Price
Bold® Stergene®	Automatic Handwashing	✓ X	Powder Liquid	Softener Wool washing	1.05 kg 500 ml	£1.09 89p

From the information:
a) Say which product is the best buy.
b) Decide which special features are important.
c) Say which product you prefer and give reasons.

6. Duvet covers　　Individual work (Design)

A duvet cover can add to the decoration of a room. Design single size duvet covers for:
a) A young child under five years of age.
b) A teenage boy.
c) A teenage girl.

Suggest suitable colours, fabrics and methods of decoration.

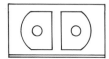

7. Fabric care

Watch the video *Not Another Soap Opera* produced by Lever Bros. It covers the topics of fabric care and care labelling.

Afterwards write out a clear list for checking a new garment or article before washing it for the first time.

Design a T-shirt like the one in the video with a care label as the motif. Display the designs in class.

Class work (Video and design)

Written work

Application of knowledge

List all the rooms in your home and suggest ten items made from textile fibres that can be found in each room.

Explaining terms

The graph on page 108 named certain furnishing fabrics. Describe the fabrics given below and say how they got their names:

- Pile fabric
- Print
- Chintz
- Jacquard
- Tapestry.

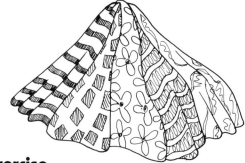

Fact finding exercise

Look at any packet of washing powder and answer the following questions from the information on the box:

1. What is the name of the washing powder?

2. What does the manufacturer claim that it can do?

3. How much powder is recommended for the main wash?

4. Why are the amounts different for hard and soft water?

5. Draw the wash code symbol for washing polycotton fabrics. Explain the bar under the tub symbol.

6. What advice is given on the packet for washing flame-resistant finishes?

7. Describe the hand care that is advised.

8. What action would you take if you had a complaint about this product?

Data response

The label illustrated was stapled to a pair of gloves.

1. What two disadvantages does this type of label have?

2. Name two other types of label that are preferable.

3. List the fibre content of the gloves giving percentages of each fibre.

4. Explain the care symbols on the label.

5. What additional care instruction is given?

6. Describe the properties of the glove fabric.

7. Explain the use of bar coding.

8. The gloves were purchased in a supermarket. Name three other types of shop where they could have been bought. Write about the changes in shopping styles in recent years.

Problem solving

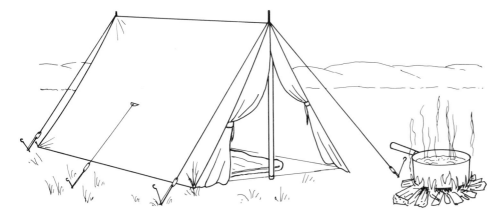

While on a camping holiday you manage to get several stains on your clothes. Describe how you will remove these stains on returning home.

1. Grass stains on your best jeans.

2. Grease on your T-shirt.

3. Chocolate on your sleeping bag.

4. Chewing gum on your jacket.

5. Blood on your handkerchief.

Application of knowledge

You have been given a hand-knitted machine washable woollen sweater for Christmas. Unfortunately there is no care label inside it and you need to know how to care for it. Find out how to do this and then make your own label by copying out and filling in the symbols below with the correct care instructions.

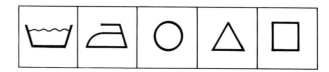

Explain the meaning of the various symbols and say why symbols are effective in a care labelling scheme.

Free response

Choosing textiles for the home requires as much thought as buying new clothes for yourself.

Do you agree with this statement? Suggest the considerations that should be taken into account when buying new loose covers for living room chairs. Explain the advantages of stretch fabrics for this purpose.

Self-assessment

Photocopy and complete the self-assessment chart on page 161, inserting the following list of topics under 'The work I have done includes':

1. Choosing textiles for the home
2. Floor coverings
3. Curtains
4. Upholstery
5. Bedding
6. Household items
7. Insulation
8. Laundering
9. Care labelling
10. Stain removal
11. Fibre content labelling.

Photocopy and complete the self marking plan on page 162 for the seven working briefs in this unit.

Consumer guidance

Core information

Consumer rights

A consumer is someone who purchases and uses goods and services. A manufacturer makes goods, a retailer sells goods and a consumer buys goods such as food, clothes, drink, homes, furniture and cars. A consumer also uses services, some of which he pays for directly but others he pays for through the poll tax, income tax or value added tax. Transport, libraries, electricity, gas, water, postal services and banks are examples of services. No matter how payment is made every consumer has a right to:

- value for their money
- a choice of goods and services
- accurate information
- safety when using goods and services
- redress for faulty goods and poor services.

Consumer information

Consumers gain information from:

- advertising • labelling • media • consumer publications.

This information should always be clear, accurate and informative.

Advertising is a communication from manufacturers, retailers and providers of services, to the consumer in order to inform, influence and persuade the consumer to buy or use the goods or services.

It can be found in:

- street hoardings • newspapers and magazines • TV • commercial radio • cinemas • shop displays • postal leaflets.

Advertisers use special techniques to sell products, for example:

- sex • life style • pets • children • family.

Advertising can have a bad effect on consumers as it can:

- persuade us to buy things that we do not need or want
- cause us to get into debt
- mislead us by exaggerated claims.

To protect us from misleading advertising there exists:

- The Advertising Standards Authority.
- The British Code of Advertising Practice.
- The Fair Trading Act.
- The Independent Broadcasting Act.

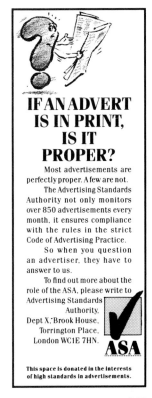

The ASA (Advertising Standards Authority) asks to be notified about misleading advertising. It aims to maintain high standards of advertising in the UK.

Advertising is big business and all firms spend a lot of money on it. Agencies are often contracted to do the advertising for large firms. Advertising space is very expensive, especially on TV at peak viewing times.

Other forms of advertising include:

- money-off coupons • free samples • trial offers • prize draw numbers • charitable causes • limited editions • free gifts
- money-back offers.

£11
DISCOUNT
Special offer—
take advantage
of our
£11 discount
with one full
payment of
£99.00.

YOUR FREE PATTERN

Y Save the Children

WAS FROM
~~£14.99~~
NOW FROM
ONLY
£12.99
plus p&p

Save £4 on
Littlewoods groceries!
Two £2 vouchers for you to use in
any of Littlewoods 68 Food Halls—
when you spend £10 or more

SPECIAL OFFER

All of these are ways of getting you to buy a product and if you like it you may buy it again once you have tried it.

Consumer advice

Advice about consumer matters can be obtained from several sources:

- Citizens Advice Bureau (CAB).
- The Consumer Association.
- National Federation of Consumer Groups.
- National Consumer Council.

Facts

- The CAB is funded by local authorities and run by volunteers.
- It can only offer free advice and information.
- The Consumer Association is funded by subscription.
- It tests, researches, investigates, compares and publishes results in its magazine *Which* as well as books on various subjects.
- The National Federation of Consumer Groups encourages and advises local groups.
- The National Consumer Council is government funded and represents the consumer at government and industrial level.

Citizens
Advice
Bureau

Consumer protection

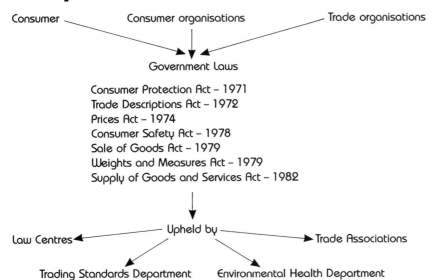

Consumer — Consumer organisations — Trade organisations

→ Government Laws

Consumer Protection Act – 1971
Trade Descriptions Act – 1972
Prices Act – 1974
Consumer Safety Act – 1978
Sale of Goods Act – 1979
Weights and Measures Act – 1979
Supply of Goods and Services Act – 1982

Upheld by

Law Centres ← Upheld by → Trade Associations

Trading Standards Department   Environmental Health Department

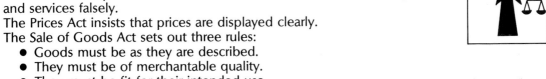

- The Consumer Protection Act and the Consumer Safety Act ban dangerous products and look after the safety aspect.
- The Trade Descriptions Act makes it a criminal offence to describe goods and services falsely.
- The Prices Act insists that prices are displayed clearly.
- The Sale of Goods Act sets out three rules:
  - Goods must be as they are described.
  - They must be of merchantable quality.
  - They must be fit for their intended use.
- The Weights and Measures Act covers correct weight and quantity.
- The Supply of Goods and Services Act controls the hiring, exchanging and refitting of goods ensuring that they are fit for use and that the work is well carried out in a reasonable time.

How to complain

A consumer should:

- Return the goods with the receipt.
- Politely explain the problem.
- Ask for an exchange or refund.
- Speak to the person in charge.
- Remain polite if there is a problem.
- Seek help and advice if necessary.

Safety labelling

Informative labelling is very important to a consumer. Certain labels indicate that a product has met certain standards of performance, safety, quality or design. The following labels are of this type.

Kitemark

Safety Mark

BEAB Approved

BEAB Approved via CCA

British Standards Institution (BSI)

The British Standards Institution is an organisation which sets out standards and tests products to see if they are fit for the purpose for which they are intended.

Each test has a number that is given to a product when it passes that test.

Goods which reach high standards are given the Kitemark, so named because of its shape. The Safety mark seen on gas and light fittings, is another BSI label indicating that they are safe to use.

British Electrotechnical Approvals Board (BEAB)

The BEAB has a new label which replaces the old familiar one which will still be seen on older electrical equipment and blankets. the new scheme has three different labels as shown. The letters CCA refer to Cenelec Certification Agreement, a European standard for electrical equipment. Products having these labels comply with Electrical equipment (safety) regulations.

British Toy and Hobby Manufacturers Association (BTMA)

A toy safety mark has been introduced by the association to indicate the toys which have been manufactured to British Standard 5665.

Electricity

The safety labels are to be found on many items of electrical equipment. It is important to understand the nature of electricity when using this equipment and to use it safely and efficiently.

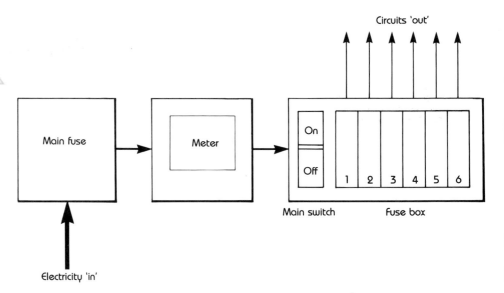

The diagram shows how electricity comes into the house through the main fuse and passes to the meter box which registers how much electricity is used. It then passes through circuits running round the house such as lights, sockets and the cooker. Each circuit has a fuse in the fuse box which will blow if there is a problem anywhere along it.

Some modern systems have circuit breakers or trip switches which shut off the electricity when a fault occurs.

Fuses

There are three types of fuse:

- a bridge fuse   • a tunnel fuse   • a cartridge fuse.

The diagram shows all three and how they are wired.

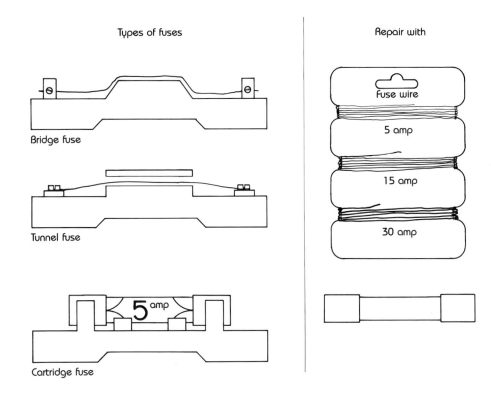

Types of fuses

Bridge fuse

Tunnel fuse

Cartridge fuse

Repair with

Fuse wire

5 amp

15 amp

30 amp

A fuse is:

- a safety device
- a weak link in a circuit which breaks first when a fault occurs.

It is important to use the correct size of fuse for the power rating of the equipment or the circuit in the fuse box.

The general rule for equipment is:

- Appliances up to 700 watts need 3 amp fuses (red).
- Appliances over 700 watts need 13 amp fuses (brown).

Circuits in the fuse box require:

- Lighting – 5 amp   • Immersion heaters – 15 amp   • Ring main – 30 amp   • Cooker – 45 amp.

If a fuse has blown in the main fuse box:

- Switch off the main switch.
- Inspect each fuse in turn.
- Repair or replace with the correct size wire or fuse.
- If the fuse continues to blow send for an electrician.

125

Plugs

Plugs should be of a good standard (BS1363). Smashproof plugs or part-insulated plugs are advisable. The plug in the diagram is a fused plug but you may still find unfused ones in use.

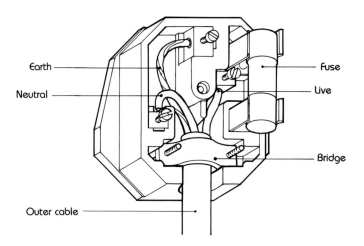

Electrical cables can be:

- 2 core (a live and neutral wire)
- 3 core (live, neutral and earth).

The cable in the diagram is a three core cable. Each separate wire is connected to the correct terminal in the plug.

The chart shows the three wires, signs, letters and wire colours.

Wire	Type	Sign	Letter	Colour
Live	Positive	+	L	Brown
Neutral	Negative	−	N	Blue
Earth	Earth	⏚	E	Green/yellow

Earthing

Earthing is necessary in order to:

- Protect the body from shock.
- Carry the electrical current to earth and safety.

The earth pin on a plug will do this if a three core cable is used and an earth wire is connected.

Electrical Safety

Electricity is safe to use if you follow a few simple rules:

- Buy electrical equipment which has the BEAB mark of safety label.
- Use BS tested plugs.
- Wire plugs correctly.
- Fit the correct size fuse.
- Use short undamaged cables.
- Switch off appliances and unplug them when not in use.
- Do not overload electric sockets.
- Keep electricity away from water.
- Get expert help with repairs.

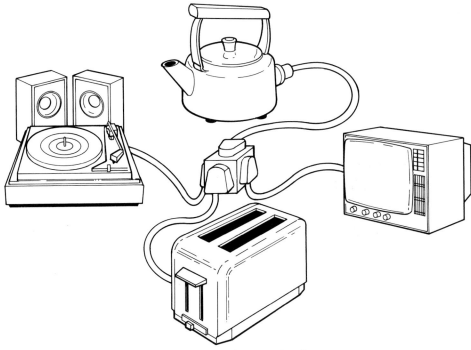

Overloading electric sockets can be dangerous

Pupil participation

Working briefs

1. Advertising
Group work (Investigation)

Divide into small groups to study different forms of advertising e.g. magazines, newspapers, direct mail advertising, TV advertising etc. Collect and bring into school examples of your area of advertising and arrange a display with your group. Appoint a spokesperson to talk to the class as a whole about your group's findings and conclusions. Groups are to move round the display areas to see the different forms of advertising.

2. Misleading adverts
Individual work (Problem solving)

Write a letter to the Advertising Standards Authority, refer to page 122. You wish to complain about a misleading advertisement which you have been a victim to, e.g. a fashion garment which turned out to be totally different from the description given in the advertisement and had to be returned.

3. Electrical equipment   Individual work (Investigation)

Look at electrical equipment at home or in school, looking particularly for:

- BSI numbers or safety labels
- BEAB labels
- Power rating labels.

Record your findings in chart form.

Model 144380
240 V ~ 800 V
complies with BS 800

BEAB

Item	BSI	BEAB	Wattage
Toaster	BS800	Mark of safety	800 W

4. Consumer information
Group work (Guest speaker and investigation)

Invite an officer of the Trading Standards Department or the Environmental Health Department to come and talk to your group about the work of their department for consumer protection.

Find out where these people can be contacted in case you ever need them. Draw up a 'Newcomer Aid' for your town or district. Include a map and on it mark:

- CAB
- Library
- Post Office
- Job Centre
- Social Services Office

- Police station
- Unemployment Benefit Office
- Doctor's surgery
- Dentist
- Schools.

Make a note of the addresses of these places and list what could be found out from each one.

5. Making a complaint   Group work (Role play)

In the following situations you will need to make a complaint about either faulty goods or services. Act out the situations before the class group who should then advise on a different approach in order to be more successful.

a) Diana bought a new pair of jeans from a chain store. When she got home she found that there was a hole in the fabric near to the back pocket. She returns to the store . . .

b) Martin was given a pair of training shoes for Christmas from a well known sports retail shop. After four weeks the soles started to come apart and so he takes them back to the shop . . .

c) Mrs Evans bought three metres of elastic from a market stall. When she got home she decided to measure the elastic and without stretching it, she found that she only had two and a half metres. She returns to the stall with the elastic . . .

6. Consumer testing
Group work (Investigation and display)

The Consumer Association carries out tests on items of equipment and then publishes the results in their magazine *Which*. Plan your own consumer testing programme in small groups, prepare the results for publication in your own class consumer magazine. For example:

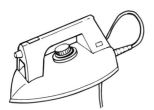 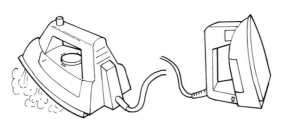 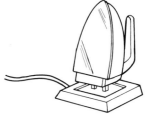

The irons illustrated are different types, makes and prices. Compare them for:

- Size
- Weight
- Handle
- Controls
- Indicators visible
- Price
- Performance.

Make recommendations for:

- Good Value
- Best Buy.

7. Consumer protection
Group work (Video, discussion and Investigation)

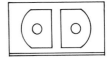

a) Watch the video *Can't buy me love* published by the Office of Fair Trading and distributed by CFL, the address is given in the Resources guide on page 160.
b) Follow up the video by discussing and deciding the important issues behind the film.
c) Find out about the work of the Office of Fair Trading and list its tasks in the protection of the consumer. You can find information in your local and school libraries.

Written work

Finding out exercise

Find out what the following letters stand for and say what job each group does in protecting the consumer:

- BEAB
- ASA
- ABLC
- ABTA
- CHC.

Application of knowledge

1. Colour in the wires of the plug with the correct colours and also colour in the fuse for the plug on a sewing machine.

2. The label below was found on a new tumble dryer. Explain its purpose and say what the letters BSI stand for.

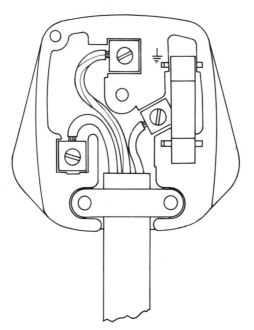

This Symbol is your Safeguard

Director BSI
Hemel Hempstead

BSI SAFETY MARK

3. Draw another label used by the BSI, name it and say how it differs from the illustrated one.

Structured question

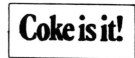

There are many different ways of advertising. One is illustrated above.

1. Name four other ways of advertising the products named in the illustration.

2. Explain the terms:
   - Manufacturer
   - Wholesaler
   - Retailer
   - Consumer.

3. The Sale of Goods Act protects the consumer in three ways, name them.

4. How can you take action against misleading advertising?

5. TV advertising is very influential. Do you agree with this statement? Say how the advertisements on TV are persuasive.

6. What are the rights of every consumer when buying goods and services?

Data response

	target price £	iron	powerbase	ease of use	verdict
Haden Wireless H6S (UK/Spain)	27	ADEG	JL[1]	□	An average performer with no convenience criticisms. Comfortable to use. GOOD VALUE
Mellerware Cordless 8075 (Italy) [2,3]	34	BC[4]	HIKL	□	Comfortable to use. Better than average performance; powerbase stability and features liked (except for flex storage). No thermal cut-out [5]
Morphy Richards Cordless 42680 (UK/Hong Kong)	29	ADEG	J	◪	Performance nothing special. Uncomfortable to use, with awkward controls and indicators. Less easy to fit iron in powerbase and not as stable
Tefal Freeline 50 (France)	35	ACDFG	L	◪	Good performance, liked the most by our users, but awkward thermostat control. WORTH THINKING ABOUT.

features

Key to iron features
A = extra steam gives a more powerful burst of steam for very dry or creased clothes.
B = variable steam control lets you alter the amount of steam produced to suit the type of fabric being ironed.
C = fabric guide on the iron shows the right temperature setting for different fabrics.
D = thermal cut-out safety feature switches off the iron if the thermostat fails. Without this, the iron could overheat and the soleplate could melt. We only recommend irons with a thermal cut-out or similar device in the Buying Guide.
E = power cleaning to remove build-up of scale with powerful burst of steam.

F = an anti-scaling device which must be removed and cleaned in vinegar.
G = jug supplied for filling iron with water.

Key to powerbase features
H = mains-on light indicates when the base is switched on at the mains.
I = iron-on indicator lights up when the iron is correctly positioned on the base and heating up.
J = clamp or screws for fixing the base to the ironing board.
K = iron can be locked into the base for storage.
L = flex can be stored either wound round or in base.

KEY TO RATINGS	■ ◪ □ ◪ ■
	best ←————→ worst

[1] Manufacturer tells us new models will have a fabric guide on the powerbase
[2] Similar model, Sona Cord Free Iron 7085, £30, cosmetic differences
[3] Tested as the Mellermatic Cordless Iron
[4] No advice on descaling in instructions; manufacturers recommend cleaning with descaling power
[5] We are urging the manufacturer to fit one in future

The report above was the result of testing a range of cordless irons.

1. Which of the irons tested is available in the UK?

2. Name the most expensive iron. How much dearer was it than the cheapest one tested?

3. Which iron was rated to be good value? Which one was worth thinking about?

4. Why was the *Morphy Richards Cordless* difficult to use?

5. Describe the features of the *Tefal Freeline 50*.

6. Explain the advantages of a power base and cordless iron.

7. Why is an anti-scaling device important in a steam iron?

Problem solving

1. You have bought a waterproof jacket for your holidays but when it rains you get wet in minutes. Suggest what you should do about the problem.

2. In the sales you bought a T-shirt which you now do not like. What can you do about it?

131

3. Your walking boots have only lasted for a few days before the sole starts to come apart from the upper. Can you return to the shop with them after you have worn them?

4. Your socks shrink when they are washed in the washing machine. The label advises you to hand wash them. What can you do about the problem?

Free response

'Consumer Safety is very important and affects everyone.'

Do you agree with this statement? Referring to the work of organisations concerned with safety, write about the importance of safety in the home and say how the consumer is protected from dangerous products on the market.

Self-assessment

Photocopy and complete the self assessment chart on page 161, inserting the following list of topics under 'The work I have done includes':

1. Consumer rights
2. Consumer information
3. Consumer advice
4. Consumer protection
5. Safety labelling
6. Electricity.

Photocopy and complete the self-marking plan on page 162 for the seven working briefs in this unit.

Creative textiles

Study Area 3

Core information

The term 'creative textiles' means using fibres, yarns and fabrics in a creative or artistic way. Using textiles creatively will enable you to:

- Create a pleasant environment.
- Gain personal satisfaction.
- Express your personality.

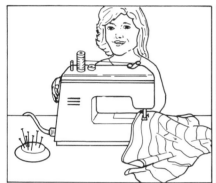

Useful hobby

Cosy home

Self expression

Traditional textile crafts have been developed over the years, using special techniques to create designs and textures. Modern methods have been introduced and new textile crafts have become as popular as the traditional ones.

Examples of traditional crafts are patchwork, quilting and appliqué. Examples of modern crafts are collage and soft sculpture.

Appliqué

Collage

Yarn techniques

Yarn can be:

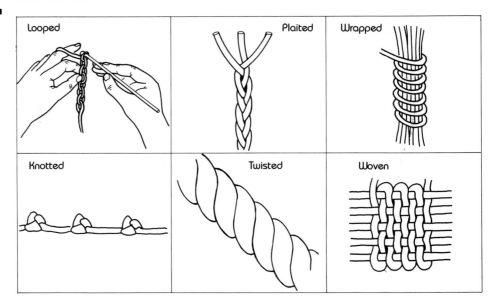

- Looping is a technique used in crochet and knitting.
- Plaiting is used to create decorative strips e.g. belts, bracelets.
- Wrapping is a technique used in collage.
- Knotting is found in macramé and tatting.
- Twisting is used for cord making.
- Weaving is a technique used for making fabric.

Fabric techniques

Fabric can be:

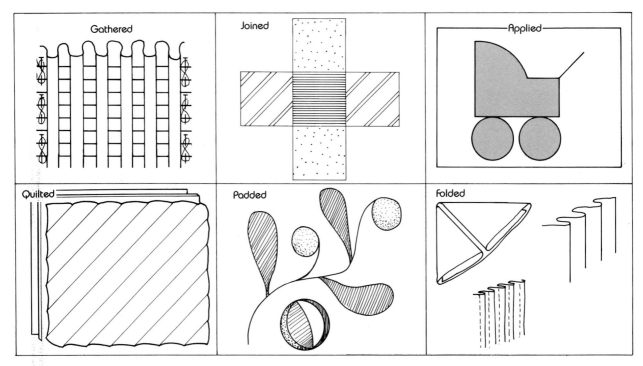

- Gathering is a technique necessary for smocking and tritik.
- Joining is used for patchwork and soft sculpture.
- Applying one fabric to another is the technique of appliqué.
- Quilting is done in different ways using more than one layer of fabric.
- Padding emphasises shaped areas of a design as in trapunto or toy making.
- Folding is a technique used in folded star patchwork, tucking and pleating.

Creative textile crafts

Macramé

The name macramé is Arabic and means an ornamental fringe. Macramé is the knotting of yarns to form designs and create fabric.

There are two basic knots:

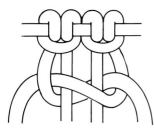

Half knot

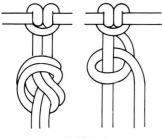

Half hitch

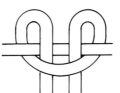

Setting on with larks heads or reverse cording

All other knots are based on these two knots and they have names such as: overhand knot, knotted chain, Turks head, Josephine knot etc. In order to start any macramé work, the yarns have to be set onto a holding cord. The knot used is called a larks head and is illustrated.

You will need:
- a macramé board   • T pins   • yarn   • scissors.

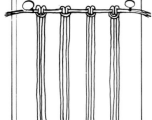

Macramé boards should be strong, smooth, light in weight and soft enough to put pins in. Special boards are available for this purpose.

Yarn should be:

● strong   ● smooth   ● twisted   ● easy to handle.

Jute, string, nylon cord and rug wool can all be used successfully.

Method

1. Cut the yarn into lengths of 8 times the finished length.
2. Cut a holding cord to fix onto the macramé board, as illustrated.
3. Set on the number of ends needed for the design, doubling each length.
4. Work the design.
5. Finish off by one of the following methods: fringing, gathering into a knot, weaving in the ends, making sinnets or columns of knots.

Uses

Macramé can be used for:

● wall hangings   ● hanging plant holders   ● mats   ● bags
● cushion covers   ● lampshades.

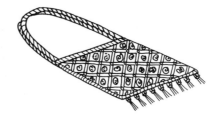
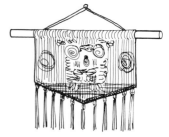

Creative weaving

Weaving can be used creatively when the fabric is also part of a textured design. Hangings, cushions, rugs, bags and other decorative articles can be made.

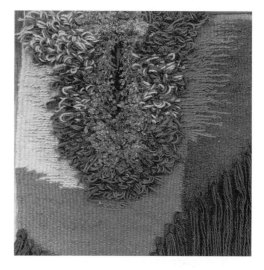

You will need:

- a frame to work on • yarn for the warp • weft yarn
- bodkin or tapestry needle • fork • oddments such as ribbon, raffia, wool, lace etc.

- The frame should be the size of the weaving, having nails along the top and bottom edges.
- Warp yarn must be strong, smooth, single and slightly elastic.
- Weft yarn can be softer, weaker, thicker and textured.

Method

1. Warp up the frame.

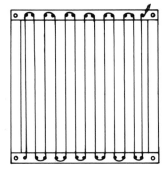 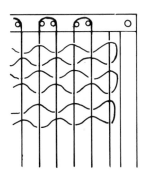 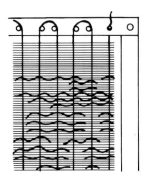

2. Work the heading which is a strip of weaving 5 cm deep. Beat into place firmly.
3. Work the design using suitable stitches and yarns in colours chosen.
4. Finish off with a band of plain weaving 5 cm deep.
5. Slip the weaving off the frame and sew in the ends.
6. Decorate the bottom edge with a fringe or tassels if suitable.

Collage

Collage is the creation of a design from fabric and thread, stuck or sewn down onto a backing fabric. A collage is made for its appearance and the technique is used for pictures and hangings.

You will need:

- background fabric • fabric scraps of different colours and textures • sewing, embroidery, textured and wool threads
- beads, buttons, rings, feathers, sequins, ribbons, lace etc. • adhesive
- stuffing, padding.

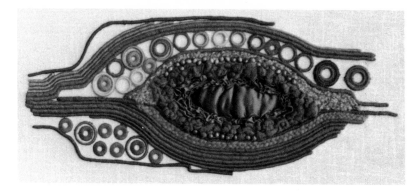

Method

1. Plan a design and draw it to size.
2. Trace off the various pattern pieces for the fabric sections.
3. Cut off the fabric sections and place them in position on a background.
4. Glue or stitch them in place and add any decoration.
5. When complete mount the collage onto stiff backing.

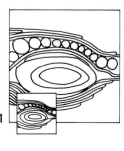
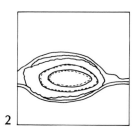
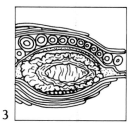

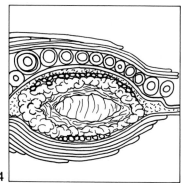
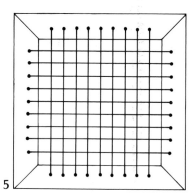

Soft sculpture

Most objects can be recreated in textiles using a 3D technique known as soft sculpture, e.g. shoes, fruit, meals, vehicles, animals, etc. Items can be given shape and form by padding, stuffing, stiffening and layering.

Simple shapes can be given depth with a fabric strip called a gusset. In this way a two-dimensional shape becomes a three-dimensional object in textile fabric.

You will need:

- fabric scraps of different colours and textures • felt or funtex – non-fraying fabrics • stuffing • sewing and embroidery threads • fabric crayons or felt pens • adhesive.

Method

1. Sketch your design and then draw it to size with a back and front view.
2. Make patterns from the drawing, including a gusset to give depth.
3. Choose the fabrics and cut out the pieces.
4. Add details to the pieces while they are still flat.
5. Join the sections together, leave an opening for the stuffing.
6. Stuff the shape and close the opening.
7. Add any finishing details.

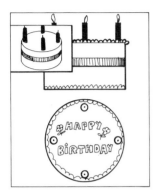 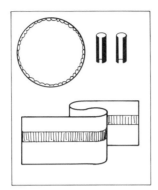 

Quilting

Quilting is an ancient craft used for decoration, warmth and its protective padding.

There are different types of quilting:

- English – wadded
- Italian – corded
- Trapunto – stuffed.

You will need:

- top fabric   • backing fabric   • wadding, padding or thick yarn
- needles or sewing machine   • thread   • frame.

English quilting

- English or wadded quilting is the decorative stitching of three layers of fabric together: a top layer, wadding and a backing fabric.
- The best top fabrics are smooth, lustrous, closely woven and of medium weight. Silks and imitation silks are popular but cottons are also used such as sateens, prints and satin cottons.
- Backing fabrics are best when made from cotton muslin, calico or lawn.
- Wadding can be of cotton or polyester and comes in different thicknesses.
- Quilting needles are short in length.
- Thread must be strong and beeswaxing can help a mercerised thread.
- Frames help to keep the work firm and different sizes can be bought.

Designs

English quilting designs can be:

- Geometric – squares, triangles etc.
- Traditional – leaves, feathers, shells etc.
- Contemporary – scenes, figures etc.

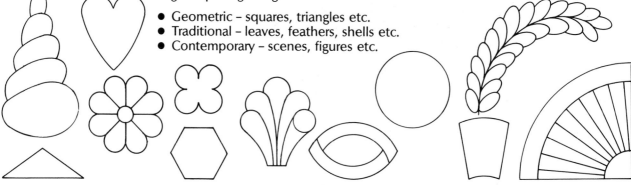

Method

1. Cut the three fabric layers: top fabric, wadding and backing.
2. Mark the design on the top fabric.
3. Tack the three layers together thoroughly as in the diagram.
4. Mount the work in a frame, stretching it tightly both ways.
5. Quilt the design starting at the centre and working outwards, passing through all three layers of fabric.

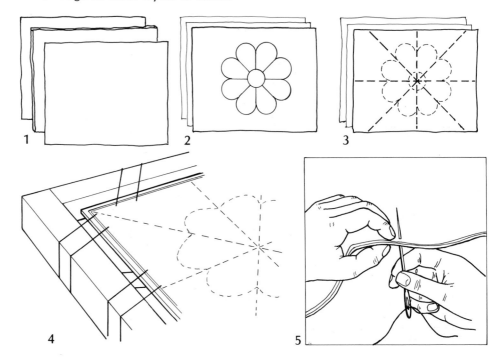

140

Italian quilting

Italian or corded quilting is worked through two layers of fabric and the designs have double lines of stitching filled with thick yarn in order to produce a raised effect. The stitching can be worked by hand or machine using similar thread to English quilting and similar fabrics.

Italian quilted cushion with trapunto rose motifs

You will need:

- top fabric
- backing fabric
- thread, mercerised or quilting
- bodkin or tapestry needle.
- needles or sewing machine
- quilting wool or thick yarn

Designs

Italian quilting designs interlock and flow more than other quilting designs. Examples are illustrated below.

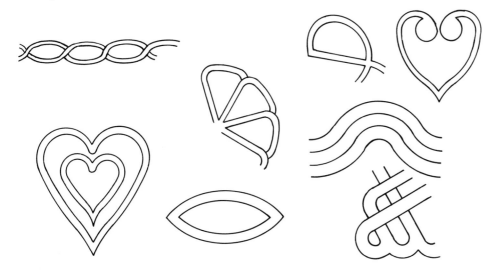

Method

1. Cut the top and backing fabric to the size needed.
2. Mark the design onto the backing fabric.
3. Tack the two layers together, cross tacking thoroughly. Stitch the design through the two layers by hand or machine.

4. Thread the quilting wool through the channels made by the stitching by inserting a needle through the backing fabric, taking care that it does not come through to the right side. When a sharp corner is reached bring the needle out of the backing fabric and go back in again, leaving a loop of yarn at that point. The loop will prevent the work from becoming puckered.

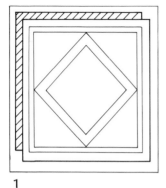
1

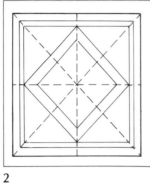
2

3

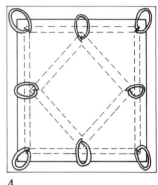
4

Trapunto

Trapunto is the name given to a padded or stuffed quilting where the motifs are raised above the level of the fabric to emphasise the design.

The outline of the design can be worked by hand or machine through two layers of fabric, a top fabric and a backing fabric. The fabric, backing, thread etc. is similar to all other types of quilting. The stuffing can be of wool, cotton or polyester fibres, depending on the type of top fabric used.

Designs with enclosed areas are suitable for trapunto quilting, such as the rose motif illustrated.

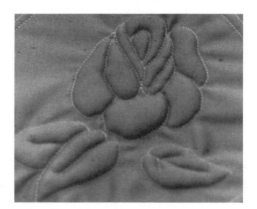

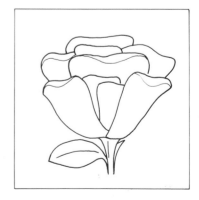

Method

1. Transfer the design onto the backing fabric.
2. Tack the top fabric and the backing together thoroughly. Work the design, stitching by hand or machine through both layers of fabric.
3. Pad out areas of the design by pushing stuffing between the backing and the top fabric through a small slit made in the backing fabric.
4. Stitch up the slits on completion.

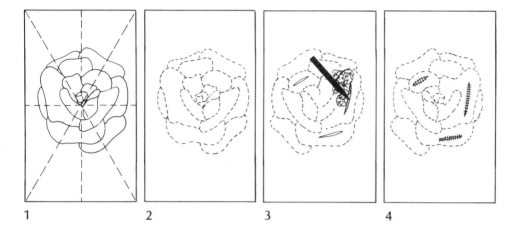

1   2   3   4

Patchwork

Patchwork was originally an economy craft which used scrap pieces of fabric and old clothes to make patches for the design. There are different types of patchwork:

- Pieced patchwork
- Applied patchwork
- Seminole patchwork
- Pleated patchwork.

You will need:

● templates   ● fabric scraps   ● stiff paper or vilene   ● needles or sewing machine   ● sewing thread.

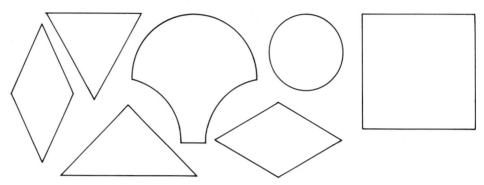

Examples of templates used for patchwork

Templates can be made from metal, plastic or cardboard. Window templates are transparent plastic with turning allowances added so that you can see through the window in order to place the template centrally on the fabric. Normal templates have no turning allowance added and are exactly to size for cutting mounting papers.

Fabrics

Fabrics suitable for patchwork are:

● cottons – plain, prints, small designs, spots, checks   ● polycottons
● silks – medium weight   ● wools – lightweight.

Pieced patchwork

Traditional method

1. Cut the patches on the straight grain. Be very accurate and cut each patch separately. Add on a turning allowance to the template size. Cut out paper templates without a turning allowance.
2. Tack each patch over a backing paper template.
3. Oversew the patches together from the wrong side.
4. Remove the tacking and backing paper and press flat.

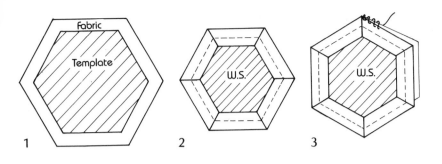
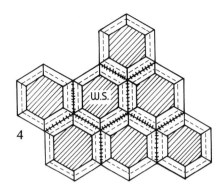

Modern method

1. Cut the patches as for the traditional method.
2. Cut iron-on *Vilene*® templates without turnings.
3. Iron the *Vilene*® onto the back of each patch.
4. Tack over the turning allowance onto the wrong side of each patch.
5. Oversew the patches together from the wrong side. Remove the tacking and press flat.

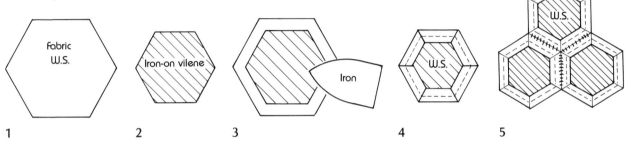

Machine-sewn patchwork

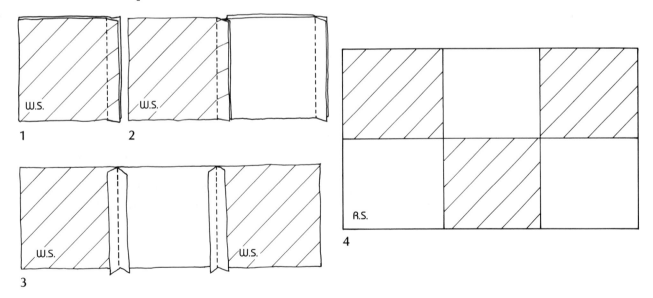

1. Using simple shapes such as squares, rectangles and triangles, cut out fabric patches with turning allowances.
2. Join the patches together in rows, machining along the seam allowance with the right sides of the fabric facing.
3. Press open all the seams.
4. Join the rows of patches together accurately ensuring that the joins match. Press open the long joining seams.

Applied patchwork – Log Cabin

Applied Patchwork is the fixing of fabric patches to a background block. 'Log Cabin' consists of fabric strips set round a central square.

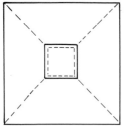 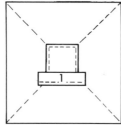 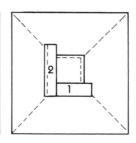 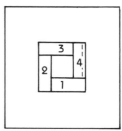 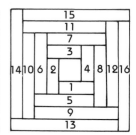

Folded star

Folding fabric into triangular shapes and applying them in a special star arrangement is the 'Folded Star' technique of patchwork.

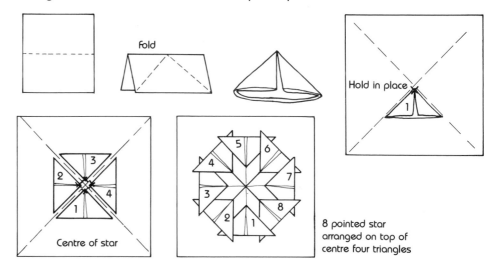

Centre of star

8 pointed star arranged on top of centre four triangles

Crazy patchwork

This method of applied patchwork consists of irregular shaped patches being applied on to a block background. Sometimes embroidery stitches are used to hold the patches in place.

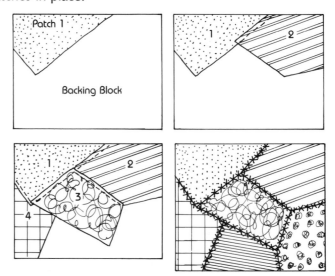

Mayflower patchwork

Also known as 'Cathedral Window', Mayflower Patchwork involves the folding of squares and folding back of edges to reveal patches of colour sewn inside. It is a different form of applied patchwork.

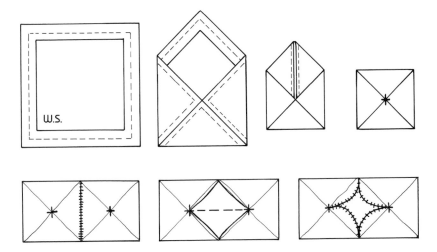

Seminole patchwork

This is a different technique as strips of patches are stitched, cut, re-arranged and restitched into intricate designs.

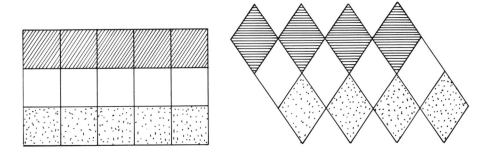

Pleated patchwork

The last of the four types of patchwork, this involves the pleating of fabric and arranging of the folds before joining the patches together into one piece.

Pupil participation

Working briefs

1. Creative textile techniques
Individual work (Investigation and design)

Design a simple motif which appeals to you. Keep to the same motif throughout the exercise.

Using different techniques such as appliqué, quilting, collage, soft sculpture, embroidery etc., work the design in appropriate fabrics, threads and techniques. Compare the different results and say which method you found the most successful and why.

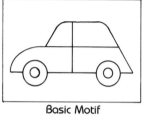

Basic Motif

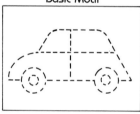

Quilting

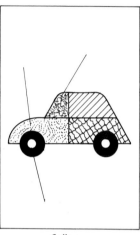

Collage

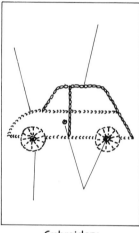

Embroidery

Appliqué

Soft sculpture

2. Craft project

Class community work

Use a traditional craft such as patchwork or quilting and plan a group project to make a quilt in sections so that each person can make at least one block or section. Join the whole article together and add the finishing touches such as edging or lining.

Give the item away as a charity effort or give it to a community project or raffle it in order to raise money for a worthy cause. Refer to the Appendices on page 158.

3. Traditional design

Some of the best examples of traditional crafts and designs are to be seen in museums and art galleries around the UK. Visit any which are near to where you live in order to see examples of design from different cultures. The Victoria and Albert Museum in London has a wealth of resources for the study of all ethnic styles, traditional colours, fabrics and designs.

4. Design

Individual work (Computer design)

Use the computer program *Mosaic* produced by AUCBE to experiment with basic patchwork shapes in order to create designs for patchwork. The colour facility makes it possible to see the effects of light and dark fabrics together and the effect of different colour schemes on each other. Below are two printouts from the program which show this.

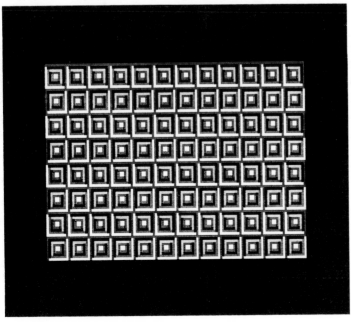

5. Design brief   Individual work (Design)

Starting from a picture postcard, holiday brochure, photograph, picture etc.
design a scene which you could make using a textile technique.
Give details of colour, texture and technique. Experiment with different ways
of creating texture before starting to make the picture.

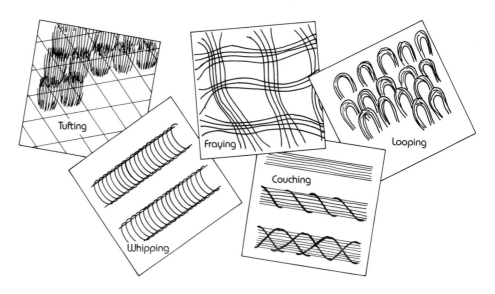

6. Design brief   Individual work (Design)

Blind children use senses other than the visual one. Consider which other
senses could be used for a toy for a blind child made from textiles. Design the
toy, stating the age for which it is intended. Describe the fabrics and any
textural effects and other special features which it may have.

Written work

Finding out exercise

Find out about and write briefly on:
- Enlarging designs.
- Methods of transferring designs onto fabric.

Explaining terms

Explain the following terms and identify the craft concerned:

- Warping up
- Casting on
- Setting on
- Framing up.

Short questions

1. Name four types of embroidery thread.

2. What are sharps, crewel and tapestry? Explain what each is used for.

3. What is soft sculpture?

4. Explain what is meant by 'straight grain' when cutting out fabric.

5. Interfacing is used to strengthen and shape textile work. Name two types of interfacing.

6. Mayflower, crazy and log cabin are all types of what?

7. Name two types of quilting.

8. Give two uses of gathers in creative textile work.

9. Knotted yarn crafts are becoming popular again. What two crafts involve the knotting of yarn?

10. Purl, rib and cable are all kinds of what?

Estimation

1. Imagine that you are making a cushion 40 cm × 40 cm with a zip opening in the centre back. The pattern pieces are shown below, seam allowances of 1.5 cm are included.

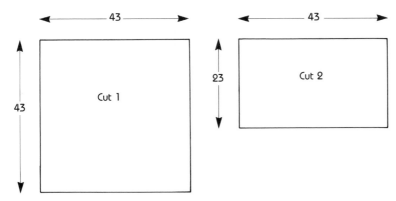

Draw the pattern pieces onto the diagram of a piece of fabric 115 cm wide and work out how much fabric will be needed to make the cushion.

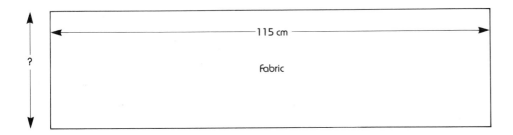

2. You are making a shopping bag from 90 cm wide cotton denim fabric, the pattern pieces are shown below.

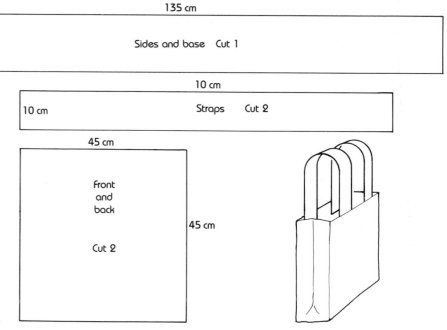

Draw the pattern pieces onto the diagram of the fabric and work out how much fabric to buy.

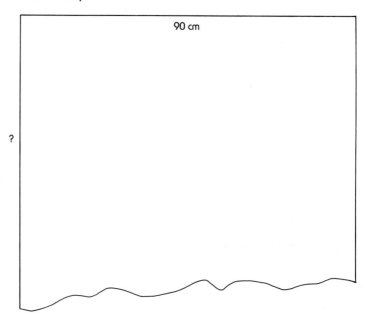

Data response

Making your own pictures can personalise your home. Many pictures can be bought in kit form from craft shops. The collage panel illustrated is one such kit. It makes a picture 20 × 38 cm and it contains everything you need to embroider the design in the kit.

Read the information on the pack and answer the following questions:

1. List exactly what is contained in the kit.

2. What is not included in the pack?

This pack contains everything you need to embroider the design:

Traced background fabric, ⚓ Anchor Stranded Cotton, needle, stitches leaflet, working chart and complete instructions for working the design. Frame and backing board for mounting are not included.

Panel size 8˝ x 15˝ (20 x 38 cm)

Bullfinches

Instructions for Working

USING ⚓ ANCHOR STRANDED COTTON

The following stitches are used: Long and Short Stitch, Satin Stitch, Stem Stitch, Straight Stitch, French Knots and Running Stitch.

The embroidery is carried with three strands of thread in the needle. Follow the coloured illustration and chart and key for the placing of the various colours.

Note.—The chart is **enlarged** so that the cyphers can be read easily.

The stitches are used as follows:—

Long and Short stitch.—Head and body of birds and upper part of wings and tail; petals of blossom.

Note.—For the sake of clarity, all the stitches cannot be shown on the chart or traced on the background. They show the area to be covered and direction of stitches. The stitches should be worked close enough to cover the background. Where 024 and 0388 are used together use one strand of former with two of latter in the needle.

Satin stitch.—Small areas in wings and tails of birds, beaks and eyes; calyx and buds of blossom and centres of flowers; portions of leaves when only one colour is shown working the outer edges irregularly to give a natural effect; dormant buds on stem.

Stem stitch.—Long lines in bird's wings and tails, dividing line on head and beaks, also legs and feet and Grey outline underneath eye of top bird; edges of leaves where outlines are shown on chart; centre vein of leaves, branches and stems.

Straight stiches.—Portions of leaves where more than one shade is used; horizontal stitches on lower portion of branch.

Running stitch.—Top of branches.

French Knots.—Stamens of flowers are Brown and high-lights in bird's eyes White with thread wrapped once round needle.

When completed press on the wrong side with a hot iron over a damp cloth.

To Make Up.—Cut a piece of stiff card to 20 × 38 cm. Place embroidery over card, fold edges to back and lace together with strong thread.

3. Explain the term 'stranded' cotton and say how many strands are used for the embroidery.

4. List the embroidery stitches used in the instructions. Describe one in detail.

5. How can you ensure the correct placing of the colours?

6. How is the picture finished off when the stitching is complete?

7. How and why is designing your own pictures better than buying a kit?

6. Free response

Textiles can add greatly to the furnishing scheme of a room and can improve the home environment generally.

Do you agree with this statement? Suggest several ways in which textiles could be used in this way. Give details of fabrics, colours and techniques.

Self-assessment

Photocopy and complete the self assessment chart on page 161, inserting the following list of topics under 'The work I have done includes':

1. Yarn techniques
2. Fabric techniques
3. Creative textile crafts – macramé
   - creative weaving
   - collage
   - soft sculpture
   - quilting
   - trapunto
   - patchwork.

Photocopy and complete the self marking plan on page 162 for the six working briefs in this unit.

Appendices – Study Area 3

Unit 1

Choosing fabric

Investigation 1 – Drape

A fabric with good drapability falls into folds easily when hung. A stiff fabric is not flexible and will not hang well.

You will need:

• samples of curtain fabrics to be tested (20 cm × 20 cm) • needle and thread • wooden pegs • drawing pins.

Method

1. Pleat each sample of curtain fabric and tack in place.

2. Weight the bottom ends with clothes pegs to hold the pleats in place.

3. Pin the fabrics to a notice board and leave to hang for 24 hours.

4. Remove the pegs and leave hanging for a further day.

5. Assess the drape of each fabric after this time.

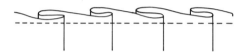

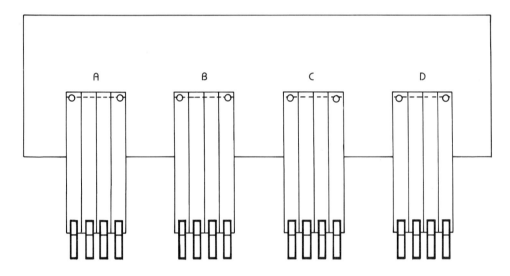

Fabric	Poor	Moderate	Good
A	*		
B		*	
C			*
D	*		

Investigation 2 – Closeness of weave

Curtains need to keep out draughts which can pass through open fabrics. This test is to see how much resistance to air penetration each of the curtain fabrics being tested has.

You will need:

• samples of curtain fabrics (10 cm × 10 cm) of different weights, disc 1 being the lightest • numbered cardboard discs • an empty toilet roll tube.

Method

1. Place curtain sample A over one end of the toilet roll tube and place the tube on top of disc 1.

2. Try to lift the disc by sucking air through the fabric.

3. Repeat with the other discs, recording the results.

4. Repeat the test with the other fabrics in turn.

5. Complete the chart by drawing conclusions about each fabric's resistance.

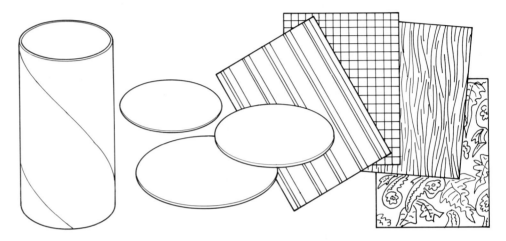

Fabric	Disc 1	Disc 2	Disc 3	Disc 4	Conclusion
A	✓	✓	✓	✗	Poor resistance
B	✗	✗	✗	✗	Windproof
C	✓	✗	✗	✗	Very good
D	✓	✓	✓	✓	Very poor

Investigation 3 – Fading

Fading can be caused by:

● sunlight   ● washing.

You will need:

● four samples of each curtain fabric (10 cm × 10 cm)   ● a large envelope
● sellotape   ● a long strip of paper   ● mild detergent   ● an automatic washing machine and powder.

Method

1. Put one sample of each curtain fabric into the envelope and seal it.

2. Carry out the fastness to light test on page **96** with another sample.

3. Wash a third sample of each fabric by hand in a mild detergent. Dry and iron the samples.

4. Machine wash the last sample with your family wash. Dry and iron it.

5. When the fading test has been completed, compare all four samples for colour loss. Record your findings.

Fabric	Control	Light fastness	Hand wash	Machine wash
A				
B				
C				
D				

Investigation 4 – Flammability

The purpose of this test is to see the reaction of each different curtain fabric being tested to flames. Testing by burning has been described on page 68 and great care must be taken when doing it. Record your findings as shown and assess the suitability of the fabrics for curtains.

Fabric	Approaching flame	In flame	Out of flame	Suitability
A				
B				
C				
D				

Unit 2

Consumer testing programme

Example: Domestic irons

You will need:

- Different types of domestic iron e.g. dry, steam, multi-feature, travel
- Different makes of iron e.g. Morphy Richards, Rowenta, Philips, Tefal etc.

Draw up a comparison chart such as the one illustrated:

Make	Type	Size	Weight	Handle	Controls	Performance	Price
Rowenta	Dry	25 cm	1 kg	Good	Good	Good	£12
Morphy Richards	Travel	16 cm	400 g	Poor	Difficult	Poor	£18

Conclusion: Good buy =
               Best value =

Unit 3

Craft project

Example: Appliquéd or quilted bed cover to Grandmothers Fan design

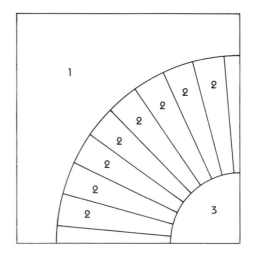

Method

1. Cut block sections for background pieces.

2. Cut fan shapes in toning fabrics.

3. Cut centre segment of the circle.

4. Give each person a block, ten sections and a centre.

5. Join all the fan shapes together by hand or machine and tack under a turning to the wrong side round the outer edge.

6. Appliqué the fan to the block.

7. Turn under a turning on the centre section and appliqué it to the fan.

8. Tack the block onto a piece of wadding and quilt through the fan shape.

9. When each person has completed their block, they must be arranged and joined together with joining strips between the blocks and round the outside edge. The whole quilt is then lined and piped to complete the cover.

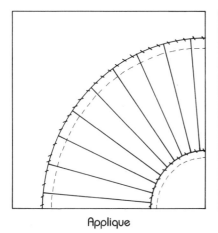

Applique

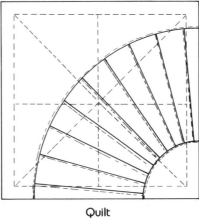

Quilt

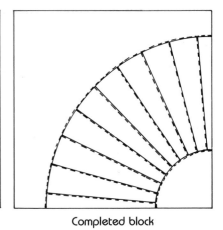

Completed block

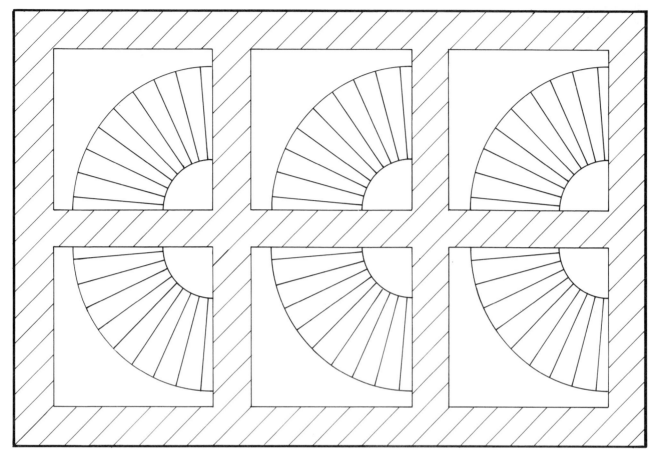

Completed bed cover

Resources guide

Useful addresses

Proctor and Gamble, PO Box IEL, City Road, Newcastle-Upon-Tyne NE99 1EL
Lever Bros, Ltd, 3 St James Road, Kingston-Upon-Thames, Surrey KT1 2BA
Shell Education Service, Shellmex House, Strand, London WC2R 0DY
Rufflette Ltd, Sharston Road, Manchester M22 4TH
Dry Cleaning Information Bureau, 178–202 Great Portland Street, London
HLCC–British Apparel Centre, 7 Swallow Place, Oxford Circus, London W1R 7AA
Proban, PO Box 80, Oldbury, Warley, West Midlands
Milium, Wellington Street, Bury, Lancs BL8 2AY
Fibreglas, 25 Berkley Square, London W1
Office of Fair Trading, Room 310C Field House, Breams Building, London
British Standards Institution, Education Section, 2 Park Street, London
Electricity Council, 30 Millbank, London SW1P 4RD
Age Concern, Bernard Sunley House, 60 Pitcairn Road, Mitcham, Surrey CR4 2LL

Books

Books	Publisher
Understanding Design in the Home, M. Picton	Blackie
Understanding Science in the Home, M. Picton	Blackie

Science in Home Economics, M. Bagshaw	Oliver and Boyd
About the House, H. McGrath	Oxford
The Home, Abbey and Poulson Box	Methuen
House and Home, B and D Lamb	Arnold
Shopping Sense, G.M. Macdonald	Forbes
Washing Wisdom, K.J. Mills	Forbes
The Care of Fabrics, M. Pattern	Ginn
Careful Consumer, J. Stewart	Heinemann
Soft Furnishings for your Home, Golden Hands	Marshall Cavendish
How to Remove Stains, Good Housekeeping	Good Housekeeping
Quilting, E. Short	Batsford
Complete Book of Patchwork and Quilting	WI Books
Basic Book of Macrame and Tatting	Octopus
Quilting, M. McNeil	Octopus
Textures in Embroidery, V. Harding	Batsford
Embroidery, New Approaches, J. Beaney	Pelham
Batsford Encyclopaedia of Embroidery Techniques	Batsford
Creative Wall Hangings and Panels, A. Babbington	David and Charles
Nuffield Home Economics	Hutchinson
Group Work in Embroidery, B. Montague	Batsford

Teaching packs

The Consumer File, Midland Bank	Forbes
Shapes & Stitches, Creative Textile Group	Nottingham Educational Supplies Ludlow Hill Road,
Patchwork Projects 1 and 2	West Bridgeford,
Quilting Programme	Nottingham
Soft Sculpture	
Weaving Programme	
Creative Textiles Scheme	

Videos

Not Another Soap Opera	Lever Bros Ltd, 3 St James Road, Kingston
Consumer Advice Video	CFL Chalfont Grove, Gerrards Cross, Bucks SL9 8TN
Maintaining Standards	ASA Guild Sound & Vision, 6 Royce Road, Peterborough PE1 5YB

Software

Soap	Lever Bros Ltd, 3 St James Road, Kingston, Surrey.
Mosaic	AUCBE, Endymion Road, Hatfield, Herts AL10 8AU

SELF-ASSESSMENT CHART

Study area

_____ **Name** _____

Unit

_____ **Date** _____

The topics I have completed include:

1. _____

2. _____

3. _____

4. _____

5. _____

6. _____

7. _____

8. _____

9. _____

10. _____

I feel confident about the following topics: _____

_____

I would like further work on: _____

_____

I found difficulty with parts of this unit because: _____

_____

Books and resources used include: _____

_____

I have visited: _____

_____

Teacher's comments: _____

_____

Study area

SELF-MARKING PLAN – PRACTICAL ASSIGNMENTS

Unit _____

Name _____

_____ **Date** _____

Analyse the skills you have used when working through the working briefs by ticking the appropriate skill on the chart below.

Skills		Working Briefs												
		1	2	3	4	5	6	7	8	9	10	11	12	13
Practical, problem solving	Planning and organising													
	Gathering information													
	Developing ideas													
	Observing													
	Considering safety													
	Manipulative skills													
	Use of simple or complex equipment													
	Presentation of work													
Interpersonal	Working with others													
	Coping with changing situations													
	Being sensitive to the needs of others													
	Listening to others													
	Talking to others													
Personal, language and numeracy	Reading and understanding													
	Writing and recording information													
	Using signs, diagrams, technical terms													
	Accurate measuring of time, cost, area, temperature, distance, shape, size, quantity													
Investigational	Comprehension													
	Analysis													
	Interpretation of knowledge													
	Selection of relevant information													
	Decision making													
	Evaluation													

When you have completed your skills analysis, you will be able to see which skills you need to make more use of.

© Gillan Jones and Stanley Thornes (Publishers) Ltd 1990, *Finding Out About Textiles*

162

FINDING OUT ABOUT TEXTILES	Common Elements			Common Themes						Skills						
	Home	Food	Textiles	Health	Safety and Protection	Efficiency	Values	Aesthetics	Interaction with Environment	Investigational	Measurement	Communication	Management	Psycho-motor	Technological	Interpersonal
FASHION																
Reasons for wearing clothes			✓	✓	✓		✓	✓	✓	✓	✓	✓				✓
Clothing styles	✓	✓	✓	✓	✓	✓	✓	✓	✓	✓		✓		✓	✓	✓
Fashion			✓				✓	✓			✓	✓	✓	✓	✓	
Haute couture			✓			✓	✓	✓				✓				
The fashion business			✓				✓	✓				✓	✓		✓	✓
The psychology of clothes			✓		✓		✓	✓	✓			✓				✓
Finding out about the history of fashion			✓			✓				✓		✓	✓			
YOU AND YOUR CLOTHES																
Line, pattern, texture, colour			✓	✓	✓			✓		✓	✓	✓	✓	✓		
Colour and its effect	✓	✓	✓	✓	✓			✓	✓	✓	✓	✓		✓		✓
Choosing colours			✓					✓		✓		✓				✓
Adding colour to your clothing																
Commercial dyes	✓		✓			✓	✓			✓	✓	✓	✓		✓	
Natural dyes	✓		✓			✓	✓	✓	✓	✓	✓	✓	✓	✓	✓	
Tie dyeing			✓			✓	✓	✓	✓	✓	✓	✓	✓	✓	✓	
Tritik			✓			✓	✓	✓	✓	✓	✓	✓	✓	✓	✓	
Batik			✓			✓	✓	✓	✓	✓	✓	✓	✓	✓	✓	
Fabric printing		✓	✓			✓	✓	✓	✓	✓	✓	✓	✓	✓		
Fabric painting			✓			✓	✓	✓	✓	✓	✓	✓	✓	✓		
Appliqué	✓	✓	✓			✓	✓	✓	✓	✓	✓	✓	✓	✓		
Hand embroidery	✓		✓			✓	✓	✓	✓	✓	✓	✓	✓	✓		
Machine embroidery	✓		✓			✓	✓	✓	✓	✓	✓	✓	✓		✓	
BUYING AND MAKING CLOTHES																
Buying clothes			✓			✓	✓				✓		✓			
Changes in shopping styles	✓	✓	✓			✓	✓		✓	✓		✓				✓

FINDING OUT ABOUT TEXTILES	Common Elements			Common Themes						Skills						
	Home	Food	Textiles	Health	Safety and Protection	Efficiency	Values	Aesthetics	Interaction with Environment	Investigational	Measurement	Communication	Management	Psycho-motor	Technological	Interpersonal
Priorities for choice	√	√	√			√	√				√	√	√			
Paying for purchases	√	√	√			√	√			√	√	√	√			
Budgeting and wardrobe planning			√	√	√	√	√	√	√	√	√	√	√			
Accessories		√					√			√	√		√	√		
Storage and care of clothes	√		√	√		√			√		√		√		√	
Making your own clothes		√			√	√	√		√	√	√	√	√	√	√	
Choosing a paper pattern		√				√	√			√		√	√		√	
Equipment and tools for sewing			√		√	√	√	√		√	√	√	√	√	√	√
Using the paper pattern			√			√				√	√		√	√	√	
Ready-to-make kits			√				√	√		√	√	√	√	√	√	
Renovating clothes			√		√			√			√		√	√		

FINDING OUT ABOUT TEXTILES	Common Elements			Common Themes						Skills						
	Home	Food	Textiles	Health	Safety and Protection	Efficiency	Values	Aesthetics	Interaction with Environment	Investigational	Measurement	Communication	Management	Psycho-motor	Technological	Interpersonal
FIBRES																
Natural fibres			✓	✓	✓			✓	✓	✓	✓					
Animal fibres																
Wool	✓		✓	✓	✓		✓	✓		✓	✓		✓			
Silk	✓		✓	✓	✓		✓	✓		✓	✓		✓			
Others	✓		✓					✓		✓	✓		✓			
Plant fibres																
Linen	✓	✓	✓	✓			✓	✓		✓	✓		✓			
Cotton	✓		✓	✓			✓	✓		✓	✓		✓			
Others	✓		✓					✓		✓	✓		✓			
Man-made fibres	✓		✓	✓	✓		✓	✓		✓	✓		✓			
Mixtures and blends	✓		✓	✓	✓	✓	✓	✓		✓	✓		✓			
World fibre use	✓		✓				✓				✓	✓				✓
YARNS AND FABRICS																
Spinning			✓			✓				✓	✓			✓	✓	✓
Thickness of yarn			✓				✓			✓	✓			✓	✓	
Textured yarns			✓				✓	✓		✓		✓	✓	✓		
Novelty yarns			✓				✓	✓		✓				✓	✓	
Fabric construction			✓			✓		✓		✓				✓	✓	
Weaving	✓		✓			✓		✓		✓				✓	✓	✓
Knitting			✓	✓		✓		✓		✓	✓			✓	✓	✓
Bonded			✓				✓	✓		✓						
Laminated			✓		✓			✓		✓						
Stretch	✓		✓	✓		✓		✓		✓	✓					
Felting	✓		✓		✓					✓				✓		
Net and lace	✓		✓					✓								

FINDING OUT ABOUT TEXTILES	Common Elements			Common Themes						Skills						
	Home	Food	Textiles	Health	Safety and Protection	Efficiency	Values	Aesthetics	Interaction with Environment	Investigational	Measurement	Communication	Management	Psycho-motor	Technological	Interpersonal
Fabric names			√							√		√				
FABRIC FINISHES																
Grey fabric			√					√							√	
Cleaning			√	√		√		√				√			√	
Colouring fabric	√		√		√			√	√	√	√	√	√	√	√	√
Dyeing	√	√	√			√		√		√	√		√	√	√	
Printing	√		√		√			√	√	√	√	√	√	√	√	√
Fabric finishes			√	√	√	√	√	√	√	√		√				

FINDING OUT ABOUT TEXTILES	Common Elements			Common Themes						Skills						
	Home	Food	Textiles	Health	Safety and Protection	Efficiency	Values	Aesthetics	Interaction with Environment	Investigational	Measurement	Communication	Management	Psycho-motor	Technological	Interpersonal
HOUSEHOLD TEXTILES																
Textiles in the home	√		√	√	√	√	√	√	√	√	√	√	√	√	√	√
Choosing textiles for the home	√		√	√	√	√	√	√	√	√		√				
Floor coverings	√		√		√	√	√	√	√	√		√				
Curtains	√		√		√	√	√	√	√	√	√	√	√	√	√	√
Upholstery	√		√		√	√	√	√	√	√	√	√	√	√	√	√
Bedding	√		√	√	√	√	√	√	√	√	√					
Duvets	√		√	√	√	√	√	√	√	√	√	√	√	√		
Household items	√	√	√	√	√	√	√	√	√	√	√	√	√	√		
Insulation	√		√			√				√		√				
Textile care	√		√	√		√				√		√	√		√	
Laundry equipment	√		√		√	√	√			√	√	√	√	√	√	√
Detergents	√		√	√		√				√	√	√	√	√	√	
Changes in home washing	√		√			√	√			√		√			√	
The washing process			√			√				√	√	√	√	√	√	
Care labelling	√	√	√			√			√	√		√				
Stain removal			√	√	√	√				√	√	√	√	√	√	√
Fibre content labelling			√	√	√	√			√	√	√	√				
CONSUMER GUIDANCE																
Consumer rights	√	√	√	√	√	√	√	√		√		√				√
Consumer information	√	√	√	√	√	√						√				√
Consumer protection	√	√	√	√	√							√				√
How to complain	√	√	√			√	√					√				√
Safety labelling	√	√	√	√	√	√						√				√
Electricity	√	√	√		√	√				√	√	√	√	√	√	√

FINDING OUT ABOUT TEXTILES	Common Elements			Common Themes						Skills						
	Home	Food	Textiles	Health	Safety and Protection	Efficiency	Values	Aesthetics	Interaction with Environment	Investigational	Measurement	Communication	Management	Psycho-motor	Technological	Interpersonal
CREATIVE TEXTILES																
Yarn techniques			√			√		√		√	√		√	√		√
Fabric techniques			√			√		√		√	√		√	√		√
Creative textile crafts																
Macramé	√		√			√	√	√	√	√	√	√	√	√		√
Creative weaving	√		√			√	√	√	√	√	√	√	√	√		
Collage	√		√			√	√	√	√	√	√	√	√	√		
Soft sculpture		√	√			√	√	√	√	√	√	√	√	√		
Quilting	√		√		√	√	√	√	√	√	√	√	√	√	√	√
Patchwork	√		√			√	√	√	√	√	√	√	√	√	√	√

Index